Patterns in the Sky

Patterns in the Sky

An Introduction to Ethnoastronomy

Stephen M. Fabian
North Central College

WAVELAND
PRESS, INC.
Prospect Heights, Illinois

For information about this book, write or call:
   Waveland Press, Inc.
   P.O. Box 400
   Prospect Heights, Illinois 60070
   (847) 634-0081
   www.waveland.com

To Tony, Tom, and Ginger, stars all,
whose guiding lights continue to shine.

Illustration credits: Figures 1, 2, and 4 from Anthony Aveni, *Stairways to the Stars: Skywatching in Three Great Ancient Cultures* © 1997 John Wiley & Sons. Reprinted by permission of John Wiley & Sons, Inc. Figure 3 from Anthony F. Aveni, *Skywatchers of Ancient Mexico* (Austin: University of Texas Press, 1980). Drawn by Peter Dunham.

Contents

Preface

This book is written with the reader in mind who has an interest in things astronomical, but not from the perspective of high-powered telescopes or advanced physics. It should also be of interest to anyone seeking non-Western perspectives on the cosmos, especially those of smaller-scale indigenous societies. As a college professor, I have crafted the work especially for accessibility and utility in the classroom. I'm especially hopeful that this work serve as a practical introduction, such that its readers will seek further knowledge on the peoples, topics, and perspectives it discusses, and offer the numerous references cited as help in that effort.

As an introductory text, this is not intended as an exhaustive study. Astronomy, as a cultural construct, is fundamentally integrated within a specific culture. To fully appreciate a specific people's astronomical system, therefore, it would be best to engage it as part of its complex cultural whole. Since such a particular cultural context and perspective is outside of the scope of this work, however, I direct the interested reader to my earlier book on the Bororo (*Space-Time of the Bororo of Brazil*), and to the many other relevant and culturally detailed works cited in the following pages.

Because systems of astronomy are so fundamentally inspired by the location, especially latitude, of a society, cultural examples are provided from as broad a range of latitude as possible. There is a decided preference, however, for specific cultural details from indigenous peoples of the Americas. Effort has been made to cite primary sources of actual fieldwork and recorded firsthand observations, but this was not always possible.

The treatment of pertinent astronomical and anthropological concepts is purposefully kept to a pragmatic level for the general reader. Technical terms are highlighted in boldface-italics in the text and are defined in the glossary immediately following the concluding chapter.

The detailed table of contents and index should help locate particular material of interest to specific readers. A limited selection of illustrations are included to aid in the grasp of key astronomical concepts, while the text itself is intended to stimulate student visualization and experiential learning through the chapter-specific exercises.

Ethnoastronomical inquiry involves intensive ethnographic fieldwork. A chapter on the main methodologies and pragmatics of such fieldwork is included in an effort to introduce proper and productive procedures and attitudes to potential fieldworkers and to help readers appreciate the process of producing much of the information included or cited in the text. This chapter is not intended as a complete guide for such fieldwork, however.

Each chapter is preceded by a brief passage descriptively presenting a relevant field experience or native story in an effort to link readers more personally with a non-Western cultural reality. I also make use of many ethnosemantic terms. In presenting such non-English words, I have occasionally simplified their original orthography. When dates are mentioned, the more culturally neutral BCE (Before the Common Era) and CE (Common Era) are used rather than BC (Before Christ) and AD (Anno Domini), respectively. Throughout the text I have attempted to write in a stimulating and engaging style for the nonspecialist, while nevertheless maintaining the accuracy of the technical explanations and the integrity of the cultural systems.

Acknowledgments

I am of the opinion that rarely, if ever, do we accomplish anything alone. Rather, embedded as we are in the complicated webbing of social relationships, we generally owe much to many. Unfortunately, even with an opportunity such as this to express genuine gratitude, it is almost certain that some deserving of thanks will be overlooked.

Although having occurred many years ago, my ethnographic fieldwork among the Bororo continues to serve as a fount of information and inspiration, and so to all the people of Garças village and Meruri go heartfelt thanks for their acceptance, collaboration, and support. Much closer in time and space, I'd like to express my appreciation to my colleagues at North Central College, and especially to Donald McVicker and Jack Shindler, for their encouragement. Also at North Central, a special thank you to June Johnson and the entire Oesterle Library staff for their competent and energetic efforts to connect me with a myriad of important references and resources. Thanks also to the publishing staff at Waveland Press, especially to Anthropology Editor Tom Curtin, for his continued interest and encouragement, and to Jeni Ogilvie for her keen editorial assistance.

Closer to home, I thank my wife, Surabela, who not only shared fieldwork with me, but functions as editor, critic, and loyal supporter all at once. The forbearance of my children, Rebecca, Julia, and Alexander, while I attend to my varied professional responsibilities, is greatly appreciated, as is the continuing support of my mother, Irene Sawka Fabian, brother Paul Fabian (whose comments on parts of the text were especially helpful), and mother-in-law, Edythe Blatt.

For reading and commenting on parts of an early draft of this work, and for his own exemplary research and writing, I thank Gary Urton. Other readers of drafts of this text include students in Farrer's "Cosmos and Cosmology" course at California State University, Chico. They are: Joanne Adams, Tammara L. Askea, Susan D. Baumeister, John D. Burge, Marcie A. Evans, Mindi H. Fox, Deanna N. Grimstead, April M. Heath, Jason T. Hicks, Glen T. Holcomb, Curtis L. Humphrey, Kelly C. McClain, Augustus J. Mendenhall, Stephen A. Pappas, Miriam L. Roeder, Mark W. Ryan, Richard Staychock, Marylisa R. Toburen, and Kristopher J. Yegge. For their comments and suggestions I am very grateful.

My intellectual debts are heaviest to the three mentors to whom this work is dedicated: Anthony F. Aveni, R. Tom Zuidema, and Claire R. Farrer. Over the years, their challenging questions, helpful comments, positive examples, and general guidance have profoundly influenced my work and life. They are truly guiding lights.

While acknowledging the help of those mentioned above, and still others unnamed, I nevertheless bear full responsibility for any shortcomings the work may have.

Introduction

As the mission jeep splashed away down the muddied trail, my wife and I were left standing with our few bundled possessions among a group of inquisitive Bororo villagers. Around us were the palm-thatched houses that formed the village circle of what was to be our home for the better part of a year, hundreds of kilometers from any town. We were in the middle of Brazil, and the entire tropical savanna seemed sodden beneath the solid gray of rainy-season skies. There was the rich smell of damp soil and wild things, an Earthiness shared by the silent forms around us. Muscular men, stout women, and their fidgeting children peered and stared at us with curiosity, disdain, or feigned disinterest marking their dark features.

In the Portuguese we shared as the bridge between our different native tongues we exchanged greetings and pleasantries, and a few hands reached out to touch us and our things. Skeletal dogs sniffed aggressively, intent on their single objective of finding some food, and bugs with the same purpose descended upon us in hordes, clouding about our eyes, ears, nose, and mouth, quickly turning every inch of exposed skin into an itching complaint.

It was while we were still there in the cleared space of the village plaza, with the fading whine of the jeep's engine and before our belongings were unpacked or even before we knew exactly where we'd be spending the night, that I was asked the first serious question by an elder of the village:

"Is it true that men have walked on the moon?"

This book is an effort to guide its readers to a more active awareness of and interaction with astronomical phenomena, while stimulating greater understanding and appreciation of native peoples' knowledge of and relations with the sky and its marvels. To do so I have relied on astronomy as observed by indigenous peoples of the Americas, owing to the limitations of scope and length of this book and to my own research experiences and familiarity with published sources. Nevertheless, the keenness of observation and the richness of native knowledge in this

1

broad geographic area, added to what is known of the significance of astronomy in such ancient cultures as those of Egypt, China, Babylon, and Neolithic Britain (see, for example, Aveni, 1989a and b, 1993, and 1997; Krupp 1978) indicate that astronomical observations and their application in cultural systems are very often fundamental to human cultures.

To adequately access, describe, and explain a system of astronomy, we need to "ground" (or, if English permitted, to "sky") ourselves in certain astronomical basics. I provide a concise overview of these basics in a general chapter and in specific chapters devoted to particular celestial phenomena. I hope that practical knowledge will be gained from actual naked eye astronomical observations, as guided by the practical, hands-on exercises and stimulated by the crosscultural examples. In this way, astronomical "facts" can be acquired, along with a growing awareness of other cultural perceptions of these facts.

Many previous crosscultural treatments of astronomy have been published (see for example, Arias de Greiff and Reichel de Von Hildebrand, 1987; Aveni, 1975, 1977, 1982, 1989a or b, 1993, and 1997; Aveni and Urton, 1982; Benson and Hoskinson, 1985; Krupp, 1978; McCaskill, 1987 [1989]; Miller, 1997; Williamson, 1981, 1984; Williamson and Farrer, 1992, to name but a few). This current work differs from these in that I have organized most of the chapters according to specific astronomical phenomena, and then proceeded to provide pertinent crosscultural examples of these phenomena. This organization, combined with the learning scenarios and an overview chapter on ethnoastronomical field methods are all intended to help make this book a practical, introductory guide to doing ethnoastronomy.

WHAT IS ETHNOASTRONOMY?

Since our beginning as a species, people around the world probably have had a strong interest in the sky and its many important and fascinating phenomena, as indicated by the Bororo elder's concerned query. After all, any time you stand outdoors, reasonably free of towering natural features or cultural structures, you are surrounded by the sky in all of its paradoxical enormity. Clouds cover it, rain falls from it, stars dot it, the sun and moon shine from it and move across it, trees grow up to it, and birds fly through it. If you spend any significant amount of time outside at all—as we did during our ten months of field study among the Bororo Indians—the sky is in your face night and day.

Not only is the sky there and in your face, but its features profoundly affect your life and what you do. Most of us still distinguish between our daytime and nighttime activities for example, and these activities have logical and historical connections to the alternating periods of light and dark—our day and night—controlled by the apparent rising and setting of the sun. In fact, our very biology has been programmed to some extent in adapting to this repeating day and night phenomenon in measurable *circadian rhythms*. And while our modern science of meteorology has come to identify numerous influences on our weather, the basic seasonal patterns of sunshine, winds, and rain still are linked generally to the sun's apparent annual motion. Nature's cycles occur in synchronous rhythm with this celestial periodicity, and any people who rely on the natural world for survival—and we only kid ourselves if we think we do not—must synchronize as well.

Today, if you wish information about what is going on weather-wise or in the sky, you can dial up information on your phone or via the Internet, turn to your local weather forecast on cable TV or the radio, or read about it in some section of your local newspaper. Data on the official time of sunrise and sunset has all been precalculated, and you can look for astronomical information in *Sky and Telescope* magazine, an almanac or other published aids, or take a college astronomy course.

But what do people do who do not have access to these resources, or who perceive the sky and its features differently from the way we do here in the United States or in Europe, in the modern West? How do other people see and understand the sky, what goes on in it, and its relationship to what happens here on the surface of the Earth? The process of finding out the answers to these questions is known as *ethnoastronomy*: the study of how people who do not ascribe to modern Western astronomical paradigms perceive, understand, and make use of their knowledge of the sky and its phenomena. A well-planned and executed ethnoastronomical project is both anthropological and interdisciplinary and ideally proceeds in a holistic manner.

Ethnoastronomy is anthropological in that it attempts to help us to understand better what it means to be human and cultural beings and does so with crosscultural sensitivity. It is also anthropological in its reliance on ethnographic or field research techniques such as participant observation and ethnographic interviews pioneered and refined by anthropologists. *Participant observation* is a field methodology that attempts to balance direct and informed observation of a people's daily life with active participation in it, real experiential learning. This process allows for the formal interview to evolve into informal and substantive conversations and dialogues.

Ethnoastronomy is also interdisciplinary, since it is best carried out with some formal training in both anthropology and astronomy, and since its subject matter can be related to so many different interest areas and disciplines, such as economics and subsistence practices, religion and ritual, philosophy, folklore, social organization, and politics. Because of this interdisciplinarity of the topic, and because from an anthropological perspective cultures can be said to be integrated in the way their component parts interconnect, an ethnoastronomical study is likely to be most productive when carried out holisitically: when astronomical details are not studied merely for their own sake but are related with sensitivity to other pertinent areas of that culture.

Ethnoastronomy is related through shared subject matter to **archaeoastronomy**, the archaeological and historical study of a people's past astronomical knowledge and related practices (see Baity, 1973 for additional, earlier definitions of both ethno- and archaeoastronomy, and the pertinent discussion by Farrer and Williamson, 1992). The research techniques most often employed in archaeoastronomy include measuring building alignments and sightlines and studying ethnohistorical documents or cultural artifacts. It is another sub- or interdiscipline, most often associated with the study of either defunct cultures (such as pharaonic Egypt) or prior phases of cultures still extant (such as the Maya and their Classic era in the first millennium CE). But the related subject matter also means that basic techniques sometimes can be shared productively in both ethnoastronomical and archaeoastronomical studies (such as in my own work among the Bororo, 1982, 1992, 1994 [1995]; Urton's study in Misminay, Peru, 1981; and the Tedlocks' work among the Maya, 1992, 1996, 1999). It is much more productive to consider the two types of study as related and overlapping, complementary parts of what can be called "cultural astronomy" (for a general discussion of cultural astronomy see Ruggles and Saunders, 1993).

THE THREAT TO INDIGENOUS ASTRONOMICAL KNOWLEDGE

Increasingly, we modern humans have built around ourselves the structures of culture, an artificial or cultural—as opposed to a natural—environment that defines and organizes us and "protects" us from the elements. But this protection removes us from nature—secludes us from it—and so impoverishes our understanding of and appreciation for both the natural environment (including the sky) and for peoples who experience and understand nature differently than do we in the modern West.

Think about it. Probably you sleep most nights in a room that is either heated or cooled by automatic temperature control. As you get up and go about your daily affairs, you probably spend most of your daytime under a roof and within four (or however many) walls: in offices, classrooms, houses, or maybe a mall or shopping center. Even for many who actively camp, "camping" is commonly in the relative security and comfort of a trailer, a roof and walls on wheels. For most of us, our movement from place to place occurs in vehicles—roofs and walls on wheels. We know little about the sky and its wonders partly because we see it so seldom and in such piecemeal fashion, glimpses here and there snatched while on the run from one interior space to the next.

Our modern Western culture, with its technology, industrialization, and urbanization is spreading globally. Indigenous and ethnic peoples around the world—people who have their own traditions and ways of understanding the world—are experiencing enormous changes in their lives. As the combination of materialism and capitalism drive our Western culture outward, external and internal forces pressure and attract native peoples to the goods, constructs, and general lifestyle of the West in a kind of push-pull effect that leaves no people untouched. Some may choose some parts and leave others, some may alter dramatically what they borrow, and some may even attempt to reject most or all of the modern West, but few can be successful at this for very long. Many peoples have not been given a choice at all.

As non-Western and indigenous peoples surround themselves increasingly with the trappings of the modern West, their perception and understanding of the world around them changes. With an increasing percentage of people living in urban areas, no longer growing or foraging food for themselves, and experiencing less and less directly the natural world, personal knowledge of this world suffers. "Modernization" comes along with heavy doses of "Westernization": occupations, education, political and social organization, belief systems, all become heavily influenced by patterns in the modern West, so much so that these become the dominant paradigms enculturated to the next generation. Old knowledge is lost: those who knew it are no longer alive, and the uses for it have largely disappeared.

THE NEED FOR A LIVING ETHNOASTRONOMY

What is lost when a people or their way of life disappears? Is it simply a quaint collection of traditions, a curious way of life? Or are we as the entire human species impoverished by the loss, the loss not only of genes, language, and cultural practices, but of an entire world of knowledge, an epistemology, the substance and the way of knowing about human existence? How much beauty, how much wisdom, do we lose?

Peoples and cultures have vanished. To a great extent, many indigenous people living today are being acculturated into the lifestyle of the modern West. Whether we perceive this as good or bad or are indifferent to the issue, once this change has occurred, these cultural systems in all of their uniqueness, complexity, and beauty and the knowledge they have acquired in specific environments will cease to be. Whole ways of life, survival strategies, and philosophical orientations will have been lost. As this occurs, it simply no longer will be possible to find or learn extinct systems of native knowledge, including systems of astronomy. Therefore, the need for a living ethnoastronomy is now, before more of this loss occurs.

Actively learning a system of ethnoastronomy is not likely to stem the tide of globalization and acculturation, nor do I mean to imply that such processes are all offensive and evil. Besides, few peoples would care to spend their lives—even if they could—as living museum exhibits, frozen in a specific set of never-changing traditions. But native lifeways are often intimately tied to a specific environment, and often rich native astronomies exist that have been used to sustain a people for generations, centuries, even millennia, as part of that environment. Because astronomy is often so integrated into indigenous culture, by pursuing an understanding of it, we will surely proceed to a deeper understanding of the people who hold it dear. Learning a people's ethnoastronomy can open the doors to true cultural understanding and appreciation of peoples both living and dead, and can enhance our comprehension of and receptivity to native environments. It can also be an inspiration for an indigenous group to retain more of its knowledge and beliefs: as representatives of the modern West, by showing genuine interest in and respect for native systems of knowledge and belief, we validate, legitimize, and reinforce these beliefs. How much more richly textured and wondrous is the human tapestry with its variegated peoples and cultures!

The chapters that follow intend to provide an introduction to ethnoastronomy, including the principal astronomical underpinnings of such a field and exercises to help learn them, representative crosscultural examples from prior ethnoastronomical studies, and suggestions for active field research. Chapter 1 sets out the basics necessary for initial orientation, both on the ground and in the sky. In chapter 2 we begin our look at specific astronomical bodies, a strategy maintained through chapter 6 and covering the sun, moon, stars and constellations, planets, and several other celestial phenomena, respectively. Each of these first six chapters includes exercises to help familiarize you with practical observational experience and knowledge. Chapters 2–6 also include astronomical and related cultural details from a broad array of societies. Chapter 7 is an overview of ethnoastronomical fieldwork, including suggestions on equipment, methodologies, and sample topics for investigation. The text then concludes with theoretical perspectives and summary.

I hope that by working through this text the reader raises his or her own level of astronomical understanding. Such knowledge is important in helping us grasp another people's astronomy. But also, by working through exercises in observational astronomy with the naked eye, you will get closer in touch with the cosmos and natural world around you, a world of wonder and beauty and tremendous power, and a world upon which we still most intimately rely for our survival. Ultimately, I hope that increasing knowledge of our own and other peoples' systems of astronomy improves our ability to live respectfully and sustainably with other peoples and the natural world that gives all of us life.

Getting to Know the Sky
The Basics

In the tropical savanna, twilight deepened quickly. Sounds of the day both in the village and beyond it changed tone and tempo. One set of biting, airborne pests replaced the other, and the villagers relaxed from their busy daytime tasks into more leisure evening activities.

"Awuri makarega!"

In his high sing-song, the Bororo village elder made his traditional cry, calling our attention and our presence. Men grabbed their mats and sauntered as shadowy silhouettes against the darkening sky to the western plaza of the village. There they spread their mats and lay prone on the cleared sandy ground, facing the afterglow of sunset and basking in the warmth of the sun-soaked earth. Cigarettes were lit and comments shared, sometimes to and from the clusters of women and children sitting outside the western arc of houses. The crier again raised his voice, talking of the day's activities and plans for the morrow over the quiet undercurrent of muted conversation.

A hushed silence followed, and then another elder's voice was heard: He told a story, an old story, a story of culture heroes and of time before and yet still now, of relations and actions and places, all known and familiar. Entranced by his voice we shared the drama of the tale, lazily waving fans of plaited palm while dogs and youths jostled for space among and around the inert male forms.

And as the story is told, and before it began and after it ends, the men lay on their backs in the plaza, looking up at a clear and crystalline sky with its myriad shimmering and colored points of light. The men lay there and beheld the stars and knew them, as untold generations of Bororo males had beheld and known them.

There is no surprise to the fact that most of us in the modern West know and relate to the sky as poorly as we do. Unlike the Bororo, who spend most of their waking time directly under the sky, alert to its various phenomena and manifestations, for us

> the skies are often smog-blanketed and otherwise obscured by towering edifices and the beaming, flashing, glaring lights that transform much of a city's night into artificial day. The rhythms of our modern world have changed, with seasonality and the observed coursing of celestial entities less crucial than business hours, banking hours, the flux of the stock exchange, and tax deadlines. (Fabian 1992:1)

To understand and appreciate fully how peoples outside of the modern West in either time or place perceive the sky, we must go beyond our astronomical ignorance. This is not a simple task, but if you have access to any observable sky and sufficient time to make periodic observations, the attempt will be well worth the effort. Entire new worlds of perception and information will open to you.

To get the most out of a crosscultural or ethnographic study of astronomy, it is necessary to have some basic knowledge of what is going on in the sky, some explanation of celestial mechanics. Few people would attempt to study an indigenous musical tradition, for example, without some formal training in music (and if they did, it would be with questionable success). While hoping to keep our minds and eyes receptive to systems of astronomy different from our own, we nevertheless need a practical understanding about motions and patterns in the sky in order to make a study of some other astronomical system truly productive. Since different peoples will have different perceptions of and explanations for celestial phenomena, learning the basics of astronomy with the naked eye within our own system can serve as a reference point from which to understand and compare other systems.

ASTRONOMICAL KNOWLEDGE AS FUNDAMENTAL

What time is your next class or that appointment you have to keep? On what day of the week did you say you would meet your friend for lunch? When does the semester end? Isn't it the weekend yet?!?

We may ask ourselves or others common questions like these daily, and yet we never stop to think how it is we know the answers. Sure, the wristwatch or wall calendar may give us the information we need, but where do those numbers and dates come from? What does it mean to be "10:00 A.M." or "noon"? How is it that today is a Wednesday, or the sixth of May? What do these names and numbers mean, and where do they come from? Whereas answering this in detail is beyond the scope of this book, suffice it to say that ultimately all such matters of time and date are tied to our Western concepts and knowledge of astronomy and the workings of the celestial sphere overhead. (For a more detailed answer that goes beyond information in the following chapters, read *Empires of Time* by Anthony F. Aveni.)

If you are a Temperate Zone farmer, you know how important good timing is to your livelihood. If you plant too early in the year, you may risk a late frost; too late, and it might get too dry, or an early freeze may hurt your crop. If you did not have a wall calendar or almanac to consult, how would you know when to plant? You would have to depend on your own observations when things seemed or looked right for planting. But would you base this on the weather getting warmer? Sometimes a February thaw comes and seems really spring-like, but how would you know it was still only February? Crops planted then could freeze before the weather truly warmed up. Perhaps you could observe when some of the early buds and blooms appear, but even these can get nipped badly by a late frost due to annual variation.

While making direct observations of events happening in your ecological environment is an important component of timing your productive and subsistence activities, the most regular and repeated annual phenomena are occurring overhead: the regular apparent movements of especially the sun and stars. Over time, careful observations of these regular phenomena—where the sun is rising or setting, for example, or what stars are just appearing or perhaps which are most overhead at sunset, midnight, or sunrise—would be your safest bet to knowing when to plant and miss the frost, based on making such astronomical observations in connection with when frosts have occurred over the years. Here in the United States, our National Climatic Center has already done this for you, and you can look up the first and last frost dates for your area in the readily available *The Old Farmer's Almanac*. In southern Indiana, for example, I do not want to plant my little house garden of vegetables before mid-April, after which I can count on about a 190-day growing season before the first frost of the fall. The Classic Maya (Aveni, 1980) and ancient Egyptians (Krupp, 1978) had their own almanacs for just such purposes, an important bureaucratic responsibility functionally significant to keeping their large populations fed.

This is fine for those growing our food. But food production—farming—has only been going on for the last 10–12 thousand years, and then not everywhere nor by all peoples. How important is calendar-type knowledge for food foragers, those who are hunting, gathering, and fishing for their food and other resources? Again, animal and plant cycles are seasonal, and seasonality is most fundamentally tied to the sun's apparent cycle. Most animals breed and give birth at specific times of the year, for example, while fish migrate and spawn seasonally, and of course flowers and fruits appear in their own time each year. If you have hunted, then you already know that there are fixed hunting seasons currently in the United States, which at least in part intend to be sensitive to game and their breeding cycles (e.g., deer fawn or give birth in May–June in southern Indiana, but active hunting is legal only in the late fall [Richard Davis, Park Naturalist, personal communication, May 1998]). While to some extent food foragers will exploit their resources circumstantially as they occur, the most effective use of natural resources is to know what is most available when and where—migrating caribou in the far north for example, returning salmon in the Pacific Northwest, or berries in the eastern Woodlands. Although astronomical observations are not the only nor necessarily the best guarantors for marking such cycles, in their annual regularity they provide a valuable gauge or checkpoint. The Crow Indians, for example, traditionally used the spring appearance of the constellation Báakkaalaxpitchee, or "Bear Above" (the Western Hercules constellation), to know it was time for trapping immature golden eagles for their prized tail feathers (McCleary, 1997:22).

In the most basic of ways, knowledge of the regular movement and patterns in the sky enhances a people's survival and livelihood. It is knowledge that is fundamental to coordinating, integrating, and synchronizing life within a natural environment, and this is important information for all of us to know: all of our lives depend on what is happening up there and how it affects us down here. Furthermore, the astronomical knowledge of a specific people, such as among the Skidi band of Pawnee, may help define that people's very identity (Chamberlain, 1982). Besides in subsistence pursuits, astronomical observations are also put to other practical and cosmological uses, such as the patterns of residences or other structures and their alignments; the configurations and orientations of whole social units; models for or coded messages on essential cultural values; mnemonics for, or texts of, or even as prominent figures in, native folklore; and ways to connect with cosmic beings perceived to be the repositories of great power.

Besides the fuller grasp of such essentials, the crosscultural study of astronomy offers itself with essential formal properties that should facilitate comparative approaches and exchange. As R. Tom Zuidema (1981a:29) has argued:

> All people observe the same primitive elements in the sky: sun, moon, and stars . . . On this primitive set of concepts people have built astronomical, cosmological, and calendar systems with as much variation as they have with kinship systems. We should be able to analyze the former systems, therefore, with the same rigorous and theoretical detail as the latter.

In other words, kinship systems, long a fascination of anthropologists, are a great subject for crosscultural study, due to their fundamental significance to society as well as to their limited and shared set of principal elements of parents, children, and siblings, which facilitates comparative research. Studying astronomical systems crossculturally similarly lends itself to comparative research due again to their shared set of basic elements. As such, ethno- and archaeoastronomy provide vital information in our efforts to understand cultural variation within our single human species.

ASTRONOMICAL KNOWLEDGE
AS CULTURALLY INTEGRATED

A people's astronomical knowledge is often fundamentally tied to economic and other productive pursuits within their natural environment, which is in itself an important enough reason to learn about it. But in fact, astronomical knowledge does not stop there: in many societies it is richly integrated in multidimensional ways with various facets of life. Anthropologists explain this in part by understanding that cultures in general are "integrated": that is, important connections are made between the way people make a living, organize themselves, and think about who they are. How this happens with astronomical knowledge is truly fascinating.

Among the Bororo, for example, Meri (Sun) and Ari (Moon) are celestial bodies, but they are also brothers and culture heroes who figure prominently in many folktales. They are related or belong to a specific clan that has, as part of its official "charge" and privilege, the responsibility to properly locate and orient the village. Not surprisingly, each Bororo village is ideally oriented with its main axis due east and west—the principal axis as well of solar and lunar apparent motion—with Sun and Moon's clan immediately adjacent to this line (Fabian, 1992). Elsewhere, stars serve as the Skidi Pawnee model for a council of chiefs (Chamberlain, 1982); the planet Venus is a deity who both empowers the sun and rises from its ashes, and is representative of an entire Classic Maya philosophic school (Aveni, 1989a; D. Tedlock, 1996); and sun and stars together, integrally associated with cardinal directionality and seasonality, serve the Mescalero Apache as the essential "base metaphor . . . the organizing principles around which Mescalero Apache life is predicated and around which such life is judged" (Farrer, 1991:17).

Astronomical knowledge is often intimately connected to how peoples not only keep and mark time and use this for their productive and extractive activities, but also with how they perceive, understand, and organize their entire world. Patterns in the sky are important in a dialectical process in which humans perceive in nature patterns that reflect their sociocultural systems; but humans also make observations of natural phenomena such as patterns in the sky and use these to inspire and fashion their sociocultural movements, relationships, and patterns on the ground.

ROTATION, REVOLUTION, AND THE RELEVANCE OF LATITUDE

All schoolchildren learn at some time that the Earth rotates on its axis, revolves around the sun, and that *latitude* is position on the Earth measured north and south of the equator. But interaction with college students for many years indicates to me that not everyone retains or is able to apply these abstract concepts to any practical understanding or use. Without getting into the full physics of the matter, these topics need to be revisited, since they are fundamental in grasping the significance of our or other peoples' astronomies.

Rotation

Let us accept the fact that the Earth, in our Western cosmology, turns or rotates in space, much like a ball or wheel on an axis. This motion accounts for much of the apparent diurnal or daily motion we see in the sun, the moon, the planets, and the stars. We see the sun "rise," but the sun is actually relatively fixed: we here on the Earth are spinning around. A complete rotation of the Earth takes place about every 24 hours, and the sunlit daytime and darker night created by this motion establish the most fundamental rhythms of our earthly world.

How long is day- or nighttime? If we use the sun's apparent rising and setting to set off day from night, those of us in temperate latitudes can still notice that some days are longer with the sun higher and longer in the sky than others. Most of the United States takes cognizance of this and reacts by changing clocks two times during the year: we go "ahead" one hour on the first Sunday in April, which gives us more daylight later in the day ("daylight savings time"), and set the clocks back an hour on the last Sunday of October. If the Earth were simply rotating on its axis in a fixed relationship to the sun, each day and night would have the same length of time. The lengthening and shortening of daytime as measured between sunrise and sunset occur due to two primary factors: the revolution of the Earth around the sun and the angle of the Earth's rotation with respect to this path of revolution.

Revolution Around the Sun

As the Earth rotates on its axis, it also revolves around the sun in an elliptical orbit, a full *revolution* resulting in our solar or tropical year of approximately 365.24 days. If the Earth rotated on an axis straight up and down or perpendicular to its line of motion, there would be little difference between day and night time over the course of the year, and little seasonal variation. But the axis of the Earth's rotation, which we reckon here on Earth through the north and south poles, is not straight up and down. Rather, it "leans" 23.5° off of perpendicular to the plane or path of the Earth's revolution around the sun.

This lean of the Earth's axis as it circles the sun results in the longer day or night phenomena, and also influences our seasons. If visualized from above the Earth's northern hemisphere, when the tilt of the Earth's axis is toward the sun, people in the north receive sunlight more directly or fully, resulting in longer days and shorter nights and the warming up of northern summer. The northern summer is "winter" to dwellers of the southern hemisphere, however, who receive less direct and shorter amounts of sunlight at this stage in the Earth's revolution. This situation reverses itself half a year later as the Earth continues to revolve. Again from our space-eyed view above the northern hemisphere, when the tilt of the Earth's axis is away from the sun, people in the north experience shorter days, longer nights, and the cooling of winter, but it becomes summer in the southern hemisphere.

Our revolution around the sun in our tilted rotation is noticeable to us on Earth by the apparent movement of the sun between its northern and southern limits and by the changing panorama of stars visible at night at different times of the year (to be covered in more detail in later chapters). When the Earth's tilt is toward the sun, most northern hemisphere dwellers see the sun apparently rising and setting farther to the north, coursing higher in the sky during the day, and taking longer to go from sunrise to sunset, events most fundamentally associated with the June solstice. Northern winters, however, are characterized by a lower sun and long nights, epitomized on the December solstice. This pattern is reversed in the southern hemisphere. (See chapter 2 for an extensive discussion of solstice.)

Observer's Latitude

It should be clear by now that where you are at any time on the Earth's surface, especially as measured by latitude or distance north and south of the equator, dramatically affects how you perceive the sky and how the sky affects you. We in the modern West divide the Earth into broad geographic zones: (1) the *Tropics* or *Torrid Zone* centering on the *equator* and stretching between the *Tropics of Cancer* and *Capricorn*; (2) the *Temperate Zone*, which extends between the Tropics and the *Arctic* and *Antarctic Circles*; and (3) the *Frigid Zone* beyond these polar circles. Although geographic, these zones are defined by solar phenomena: the Tropic of Cancer is 23.5° (more accurately, 23° 27') north of the equator, and the Tropic of Capricorn is the same angular distance south. These lines mark the farthest limit north or south of the equator from where the sun can be seen to stand at the **zenith** (or the point of sky directly overhead) at its farthest apparent northern and southern extreme. The Arctic and Antarctic Circles, respectively at 66.5° (more accurately, 66° 33') north and south of the equator, are the lines beyond which the sun will not be seen when it reaches its apparent southern and northern extremes, respectively, or will not set at its apparent northern and southern extremes.

Not only will the sun enter different parts of the sky when viewed from different latitudes, but the angle of its apparent movement also differs. For viewers in the Torrid Zone or the Tropics, the apparent daily path of the sun is a vertical or nearly vertical line. For Temperate Zone viewers, however, the sun has a more acute angle of apparent motion, while for viewers in the Frigid Zone the sun's angle of apparent motion is flatter still. Not only is the angle of the sun's apparent motion latitude sensitive, but its direction of apparent motion as well. In the book *Black Elk Speaks*, this famed Lakota (Sioux) holy man refers to movement of rituals occurring in a "sunwise" direction (Neihardt 1979 [1932]). Since he is an observer in the north Temperate Zone, we know that sunwise for Black Elk meant moving from left to right, or what we commonly refer to as "clockwise." Sunwise motion for anyone in the south Temperate Zone, however, would be just the opposite: although the sun still rises in the east and sets in the west, it passes through the northern portion of the sky, therefore appearing to move from right to left or in a counterclockwise direction. For people directly on the equator, "sunwise" would need seasonal clarification, since for each half of the year they can observe the sun going in either of the sunwise directions! (More discussion of the sun's motion occurs in chapter 2.)

So what you may have considered as a fairly routine phenomenon—the rising and setting of the sun—turns out to be quite a bit more complicated when looked at from different location-based perspectives. But heightening your awareness of this type of difference is much of what this book is about.

While the above discussion centers mainly on the sun and our perceptions of its motion, the observer's latitude and the effects of rotation and revolution affect *everything* he or she sees in the sky, as will become apparent in the following chapters.

LOCATING CELESTIAL OBJECTS

If you are anxious to get started in making astronomical observations, you need do nothing other than get outside on the first clear day and night and simply become more aware of what is in the sky. To help you understand what you are seeing, it is advisable to visit your local library, bookstore, and/or personal computer. Helpful resources include the magazines *Sky and Telescope* or *Astronomy*, both with monthly sky maps and information on what is up there, and any one of a variety of relatively inexpensive and portable guide books, such as *Field Guide to the Stars and Planets,* by Donald Menzel (Peterson Field Guide Series), or the *Pocket Guide to Astronomy*, by Patrick Moore. Or get help from your computer: try Montenbruck's *Astronomy on the Personal Computer* and any of various software programs, such as "The Sky Astronomy Software for Windows" (see Aveni, 1997, Appendix C, for additional suggestions). From *Sky and Telescope's* publishers you can also order a handy adjustable star gazer that will help you identify stars and constellations at your latitude throughout the night and year. Some newspapers print pertinent astronomical information, while helpful Web sites also exist, such as that of the Adler Planetarium in Chicago (http://www.adlerplanetarium.org). Of course, a visit to any planetarium or observatory is also highly recommended.

To get started on your own, you will need to get oriented, so be sure to take note of sunrise or sunset to mark east and west. North and south run perpendicular to the east-west line, of course, and can be precisely fixed by locating the region of the celestial pole at night, conveniently marked closely by Polaris or the North Star for northern latitude observers, while it is encircled by the Southern Cross in the southern hemisphere. (Tips for locating the celestial poles are included in the exercises section of chapter 4.) A magnetic compass can help you get oriented initially, but remember that a magnetic compass indicates *magnetic*—not true—north.

HORIZON-BASED MEASUREMENTS: AZIMUTH AND ALTITUDE

Once you can begin to identify and locate celestial objects, you will want to record what you see. Although systems of astronomical coordinates exist that fix the location of objects in a universal celestial system (like terrestrial latitude and longitude for locations on the Earth), naked eye astronomy is most relevant to localized contexts and purposes. Therefore, the most convenient system of coordinates for your local observations is that described as horizon-based, and includes azimuth and altitude.

Informally, the horizon is wherever the sky appears to meet the ground. For measurement purposes, however, it is helpful to consider an "ideal" horizon as what you would see if there were no hills, trees, houses, or other obstructions between you and a view of the flat line of intersection of Earth and sky. *Altitude* of any celestial object is simply measured vertically up from this ideal horizon, to the maximum 90° at the zenith, the point directly overhead. *Azimuth* measures the position of an object in the sky starting from true north as 0° and continuing to the right (or eastward/clockwise) through 360° of arc back to north: east = 90°, south = 180°, and west = 270°.

Note: until now, references have been made to celestial motion by qualifying perceived movement as "apparent" (as in "the apparent rising and setting of the sun," only apparent since technically the sun is not rising, the Earth is rotating). This can get cumbersome. So, having reviewed the basics of terrestrial axial rotation and revolution around the sun, succeeding passages will assume that the reader is familiar with the basics of celestial mechanics and will describe celestial motion mostly as we Earth-based observers perceive it (e.g., the sun rises in the east).

More relevant astronomical explanations are provided in the upcoming chapters. But it is time to get a real look at and feel for the sky.

THE OBSERVATION NOTEBOOK

In order to get a practical understanding of what is going on in the sky, it is helpful to make and record a number of astronomical observations over a period of time, such as over a season or school semester. By recording these observations in a notebook or collecting them in a single folder you will find it easier to compare your observations and learn from their differences. Patterns will begin to emerge. Rather than purchase a ready-made observation journal, you can use any standard-size notebook for recording your observations. You can even use the lines in a ruled tablet to help in scaling altitude or azimuth measurements (graph paper too can work, but it sometimes has so many dark lines that they obscure the drawing of your observations).

To be useful, recordings of observations must contain certain specific information. Each record must include:

1. the date;
2. the time of your observation;
3. the location from which you made your observation;
4. the altitude of what you are observing;
5. the azimuth of what you are observing;
6. a relevant horizon line and estimate of its altitude (except when making observations of or near the zenith); and
7. an identification (as best you can) of what you have observed and recorded.

Your drawings and recorded information should be as accurate as possible and clear to understand. It is helpful to sketch in the local horizon (including obstructions and elevations), and it is also convenient to plot a span of altitude and azimuth estimates along the vertical and horizontal edges, respectively, of the page.

Besides your notebook, pencil and eraser, and any star or sky charts you might be using for reference, at night you will need a flashlight to make your drawings or read from your reference charts. When using the flashlight in this way, be sure to dim its light by securing some red cellophane over the lens. (Try your local arts and crafts store for the cellophane. An Army/Navy surplus store or sporting goods shop might carry flashlights with a replaceable red lens for night vision use. If all else fails, use a red handkerchief or other colored cloth to dim your light; a rubberband works great for fastening cellophane or cloth.) If you are working in a group, a strong, undimmed flashlight can be used as a pointer to clarify which star is being discussed and to trace constellation patterns or other stellar connections. And dress for the weather. Nocturnal observation sessions can be damp and cold, and if you are too uncomfortable, the quality of your observations will suffer.

EXERCISES: THE OBSERVATION PROCESS

Exercise 1.1   Orienting yourself to the sky at your latitude, and finding a good "observatory"

This exercise is somewhat like swishing your foot in the swimming pool to test the waters before jumping in. Simply go out and look at the sky and what is in it. If it is daytime, take note of the sun's position (but WARNING! never look directly at the bright orb of the sun; it can damage your eyes). Is it in the northern or southern part of the sky? Is it closer to east or west, or more overhead? Take note of the time, and then compare your observations an hour or two later. How much change has occurred? If there are clouds out, in what direction are they moving? Is it the same later that day or the next day?

If it is night, just get a sense of the brightness, number, colors, and patterns of stars overhead, take note of the time, and again compare your observations an hour or two later.

If it is night or day, is the moon out (yes, the moon is often visible in the day sky!)? Where is it, and what is its shape? Where is it an hour or two later, and is its shape the same? What is its position relative to the sun? Compare your observations with those made a day or two or week later.

To make good observations consistently and with best comparative results, it is desirable to find a place from where you can make your observations with the least amount of artificial light, horizon obstructions and other distractions (seasonal and local weather patterns will also greatly determine sky visibility and the conditions in which you are observing the sky). You may want or need to select more than one "observatory." A site from which sunset observations are good, for example, may not be best for observations to the east or overhead. Remember, isolated observations that are not followed up by subsequent comparative observations provide little information: "*Information* consists of differences that make a difference" (Bateson, 1979:110). Try to find patterns. To further your awareness of patterns, try this exercise again at the same time two weeks later.

Exercise 1.2 Working with concepts: the north or south celestial pole, the celestial equator, the zenith and the meridian

As already reviewed, the Earth rotates on its axis, a line marked on the globe by the north and south poles. By extending these poles into the infinitude of the cosmos, we can imagine a **north celestial pole** (NCP) and a **south celestial pole** (SCP). These points form the axis around which the sky appears to rotate. For a northern latitude observer, the NCP is conveniently marked by Polaris. The SCP, unfortunately, is not marked by any comparably bright star; the prominent constellation of the Southern Cross is often used as an aid in the pole's location. Although more help in stellar identification is provided in chapter 4, know this simple rule: the altitude of the celestial pole is equivalent to the observer's latitude. In other words, if you are at about 40° north latitude (N) (e.g., near cities such as Reno, Denver, Indianapolis, Philadelphia), Polaris and the NCP will be up just short of halfway between the ideal horizon and your local zenith, the point in the sky directly overhead.

Finding the NCP or SCP is fundamental, not only as an important identification in itself or even for basic orientation, but also because by knowing where the NCP or SCP is located, you will also have a clearer sense of the sky's rotation. Working with the sky as a sort of celestial sphere or globe (with us on the inside), we can imagine that halfway between the NCP and SCP and perpendicular to their axis is a line or plane called the **celestial equator**, analogous to the terrestrial equator. The celestial equator is a helpful concept to the naked eye astronomer because all regular rotation occurs in lines that are along or parallel to this line, on imaginary planes perpendicular to and circling around the axis connecting the NCP with the SCP.

One last celestial concept that will be helpful at this beginning stage is that of **meridian**. If you have found the NCP or SCP (and as a reminder, only someone directly on the equator with an absolutely level horizon might be able to see both of these at once), then trace the line from north horizon point to south horizon point, through the pole and your personal zenith. This imaginary line that bifurcates the sky is the meridian. It is important because it marks the highest point in the arc of any celestial object's rotation. When the sun is on it, the time is noon.

Exercise 1.3   *Measuring by hand and eye*

Once you begin your observations and recordings, you will need some system of gauging degrees of arc. Your unaided eye can be quite good once trained at estimating such angular distances; for example, if you judge something to be halfway between horizon and zenith, then it is about 45° up. Further help is provided by a "handy" measuring device you carry with you: your hand. At arm's length, an observer's extended, open-palm hand (with the thumb-side pointing up and the palm facing the observer) or an observer's closed fist measures about 10° of arc. Try this: hold your right, open-palm hand or your fist straight out at arm's length at ideal horizon height; now place your extended, open-palm left hand on the top of your right hand, or your left or fist on top of your right fist. Then, without moving your left hand or fist put your right one on it. Continue alternating your hands vertically to the zenith. How many palms or fists did it take?

One other observational tip: the orb of the sun or full moon up in the sky measures about 30 minutes or 1/2° of arc. (Near or on the horizon, however, there may be size distortion due to atmospheric and other effects on our perception.)

Try your new measuring aid on a variety of informal observations.

Chapter Two

The Sun

Among the Bororo, Meri (Sun) is known as older brother to Ari (Moon), and the two of them, often referred to as Meri-doge (plural of Meri), traveled together, sometimes playing pranks on the Bororo.

One day, after many encounters with the Bororo, the Meri-doge were thirsty. They stopped at the house of members of the Iwagududoge clan (localized on the southwest arc of the village circle of houses) who were associated with large aquatic birds (*karawoe*). The Meri-doge asked for water, which was kept in large and heavy ceramic jars. Knowing the brothers' mischievous inclination, the Karawoe were reluctant to let them handle the valuable water jars. When Meri picked up a jar to drink, his hosts said: "Father, do not do that, you will break the jar."

"No, I will not break it."

But no sooner had he said these words when the jar slipped from Meri's hands to the ground, breaking into many pieces.

"We told you that you would break it!"

Hearing their angry complaints, Meri and Ari fled, pursued by the Karawoe who caught them and brought them back to their house. The Meri-doge were made to sit next to each other in the midst of the Karawoe, who began to fan them with fans of plaited palm.

The Meri-doge complained: "Don't make wind like that."

But the Karawoe replied, "You produce a lot of heat."

And they kept fanning with so much force that Meri and Ari were lifted by the wind into the sky.[1]

There is no regular celestial phenomenon that is so obvious or as consequential for us here on Earth, as the sun. The very life processes of all terrestrial organisms are utterly dependent on solar energy and the rhythms associated with our daily rotation and yearly revolution. Indeed, the sun is such a powerful and obvious natural phenomenon that it is difficult to imagine the native society that has not observed it with great interest.

DAILY MOTION

For us as Earth-based observers, the sun's predominant motion is a daily rising in the east and setting in the west. But its course varies greatly depending on the observer's latitude. For someone on the equator (0° latitude), the sun will appear to pop up out of the horizon and rise straight up, peak high up at noon as it crosses the meridian either north or south of the zenith, and vertically descend to its setting place. Although once off the equator the sun's daily motion may not be precisely straight up and down, the tropical band is characterized by vertical daily solar motion, high noontime sun with very short noontime shadows, and short periods of twilight (prerise dawn and postset dusk).

By comparison, in the Temperate Zones the sun's daily path forms more of an acute angle with the horizon. The sun rises more gradually as it slides along the horizon, climbs at a slant to its noontime meridian peak, which will always be either north or south of the zenith depending on the hemisphere (south or north, respectively) of the observer, then coasts back down its descent ramp, skimming along the horizon to its eventual set. While the angle of motion is much more acute near the northern and southern temperate fringes close to the Arctic and Antarctic Circles, in general the Temperate Zones are characterized by slanted daily solar motion, medium-high noontime sun and noticeable noontime shadows, and extended periods of twilight.

The far north and south or Frigid Zones have few permanent residents: most of Alaska and Canada is still technically temperate, and Tierra del Fuego, South America's southern tip, is short some 10° from the Antarctic Circle. Residents north of the Arctic Circle observe the daily motion of the sun as a flattened path circling around the sky rather than traveling up and down. The sun will be low in the sky, will skim along the horizon at and near the equinoxes, and will not be visible at all for some time on either side of the solstices (December in the north and June in the south). Here the sun stays low and shadows are long, with prolonged periods of light, twilight, and darkness alternating throughout the year.

THE SOLAR YEAR:
SOLSTICES, EQUINOXES, AND THE SEASONS

It has already been mentioned that the Earth is tilted on its axis about 23.5° to its plane of revolution, and that it pursues an elliptical revolution around the sun that takes about 365 days (closer to 365.24).

Because of these factors, the daily motion of the sun as we perceive it varies over the course of a year. As the sun pursues its yearly travels along the *ecliptic*, its apparent path against the stars, at different times of the year it is either higher or lower in the sky, further north or south, and the days (or nights) are longer or shorter.

Our Western (Gregorian) calendar identifies four seasons or divisions of the year considered "natural" in the temperate zone in which our modern calendar developed. The four seasons are reckoned informally by changes in weather patterns and are associated culturally with season-specific activities. Astronomically, the four seasons currently recognized are marked by the sun's position in its northern and southern extremes, the solstices; and near its midpoint between these extremes when day and night time are approximately equal, the equinoxes. The term *solstice* derives from the Latin for "sun" (sol) and "to stand" (sistere), an expression that nicely describes the sun on and around June 21–22 and December 21–22, the dates for its northernmost and southernmost extreme positions, respectively. For several days at these times in the year the sun will appear to rise and set in the same places and attain the same altitude at noon. This apparent "stand still" occurs after the sun can be seen approaching these limits either along the horizon or via its height at noon as measured by shadow casting.

After reaching either solstitial extreme the sun begins to reverse its motion, slowly at first with very little difference in its rising or setting location or its path in the sky. Gradually, the sun seems to quicken its pace until near the *equinoxes*—on or around March 22 and September 22—when its daily rising and setting locations are farther apart, as is its height in the sky. After this, it will again gradually "slow down" as it approaches the opposite extreme. These north to south peregrinations of the sun are directly responsible for seasonal phenomena, and are noted with interest by many native peoples. Bororo elders know the sun's horizon extremes as seen from the village plaza, and several Bororo myths recount travels of the Meri-doge, the sun and moon as anthropomorphized culture heroes.

For observers in the north Temperate Zone, winter begins on or near December 21. On this date night is the longest and daylight the shortest, and the sun courses relatively low in the southern portion of the sky, even at noon; for an observer at 40° north latitude (N), for example, the altitude of the noon sun at the December solstice will be only about 26.5°. Nights get shorter and days longer as the sun moves northward. On or around March 22, the vernal equinox, which begins our northern spring, the sun rises approximately due east and sets due west, and daytime and nighttime are approximately equal (equinox derives from the Latin for "equal night"). On the equinox, the noon sun for our same 40° N observer will have an altitude of about 50°. Continuing its move northward along the horizon the sun is also observed higher in the sky. The sun gradually achieves its northern extreme on June 21–22, and summer officially begins. As it "stands still" in June, its altitude at noon observed from 40° N will be about 73.5°. We will then see the sun swing back to the south, through its east-west position of the September equinox on or around the 22nd (the beginning of our fall or autumn), after which the shortened days and lower daytime sun become more obvious, until winter officially begins again with the December solstice.

Solstice extremes are important to many temperate peoples. Although New Year celebrations in our Gregorian calendar may seem impractical for northern temperate dwellers caught in the cold and snow of early winter, how fitting it seems to celebrate a new year once the sun has definitively turned in its course. Northern latitude observers see the sun progress ever southward in December, as the days shorten and the cold of winter arrives. With several winter months ahead, what a relief to observe the sun cease its southward course and begin again to advance northward, with the promise (at least) of a warm spring and summer yet to come.

The Tewa, a Puebloan society in the U.S. Southwest, celebrate the "days of the sun," the "final work of the year," in mid-December, which is "a winter solstice and new year rite in which the whole community participates" (Ortiz, 1969:102). Boas reports that for some Central Eskimo (some of whom are above the Arctic Circle), a type of "new fire" ceremony is practiced around the time of the December solstice (1888:607–8). In Washington State, in the Northwest Coastal area, the native Quinault are described as setting up observation "seats" from which to observe solstice sun rises and sets. While the June solstice went unnamed, the "winter solstice was called xa'Ltaanm (comes back, the sun) (Olson as quoted in Miller, 1992:194). At this time, Quinault whalers "made contact with their supernatural patron" (Miller, 1992:195). McCleary (1997) reports that for the Crow the winter or December solstice is traditionally "a time of social and religious significance" and a time when special social winter dances are held (103).

June solstice, as the time when the sun is highest and the days are longest, is also an important time in traditional northern calendars. For Northern Plains Indians, the June solstice was the time for a religious ceremony of great importance, the Sun Dance. As Black Elk describes it, it was a dance "to purify the people and to give them power and endurance. It was held in the Moon of Fatness [June, more or less] because that is the time when the sun is highest and the growing power of the world is strongest" (Neihardt, 1979 [1932]:96). Perhaps for similar reasons the June solstice was the traditional time for performing the Apache girls' puberty ceremony, although today the event occurs for practical purposes during the Fourth of July weekend. That this Apache ceremony is linked to solar significance is clear in the activities of its fourth and last day, especially the blessing time called "pulling the sun": after a full

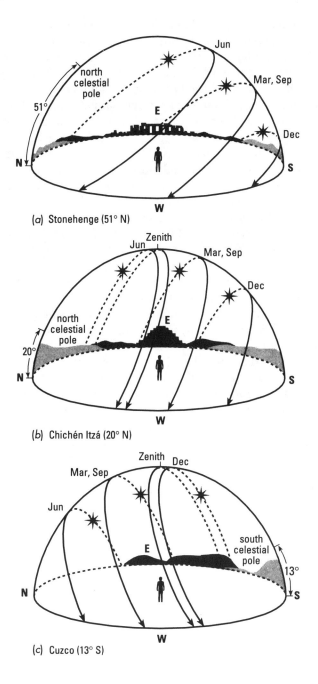

(a) Stonehenge (51° N)

(b) Chichén Itzá (20° N)

(c) Cuzco (13° S)

Figure 1. The daily path of the sun on March 20, June 21, September 22, and December 21 as seen from (a) Stonehenge (latitude 51° north), (b) Chichén Itzá in northern Yucatan (latitude 20° north), and (c) Cuzco, Peru (latitude 13° south). Additional lines in (b) and (c) show the path on zenith passage dates.

night of ceremonial activity and nearing sunrise approaches, "as the last verse of the last song is sung, [the singers/ritual specialists] extend their arms over their heads, with their palms, the sun symbols painted on them, open and facing toward the sun." If the timing and singing are correct, "just as the last note of the last morning song is sung, the sun tops the mountains to strike the men's upraised palms" (Farrer, 1996:85).

The solstices together may form a significant marker of annual periodicity, a bisecting of the year. As Hultkrantz (1998 [1987]) describes for the Southwestern Zuni, "the ritual year is divided into two halves separated by the winter and summer solstices. The winter and spring ceremonies are concerned with medicine, war, and fertility; the summer and fall ceremonies with rain and crops" (120).

Observing the solstices as the critical points in the sun's path when it reaches its extremes and reverses its direction is important to many native peoples. Fortunately, since the sun appears to move relatively slowly or change its position minimally in the days preceding the actual solstice, it is a time relatively readily observable in the sun's cycle. What about the equinoxes, the dates we use in combination with the solstices to determine the formal seasons in our contemporary Gregorian calendar? Since the sun is moving rather more quickly with greater daily change in its position in March and September than it is in June and December, are the equinoxes important dates in traditional northern calendars? How are they determined? Chamberlain (1982) suggests that for the ethnohistoric Skidi Pawnee the rising sun on the equinoxes was important in lighting up the interior altars of their east-oriented lodges through a small entranceway (179). McCleary (1997) observes that the Crow hold the equinoxes as "ritually significant" for the first annual splashes of water in the sweatlodge (103). But whether the equinox was determined by or itself determined the east-west direction is unclear. Among the Tewa, the time from the autumnal equinox through the vernal equinox is the period of the year most ritually active, and is contrasted with the heightened agricultural activity from vernal to autumnal equinox (Ortiz, 1969:104–5). On the other side of the world the importance of the equinoxes is inscribed in the Japanese calendar, where to this day the vernal and autumnal equinoxes—historically significant and meticulously observed by Chinese and later Japanese astronomers—serve as national holidays.

THE TROPICAL SUN: ZENITH PASSAGE AND ITS COMPLEMENT, THE NADIR

In the Tropics, the sun also is observed to sweep between northern and southern horizon extremes and relatively high and low noon positions overhead, but with some significant differences to the picture as presented for the Temperate Zone observer. Whereas for the northern observer the sun is at its lowest at the December solstice, for the tropical but southern latitude Bororo—who inhabit areas of Mato Grosso, Brazil, between about 15° and 19° South Latitude—the noon December solstice sun stands at over 80° altitude, south of the zenith. As it turns around on its return trip to the north, the noon sun actually gets higher, peaking at noon in early February at the zenith itself, casting no shadow from upright objects at noon. It descends from the zenith daily after that, but is still over 70° high at noon at the March equinox, now to the north of the zenith. Its lowest noontime height, during the June solstice, still has it at over 50° of altitude in the northern sky. The sun will then pass again through the zenith in November en route to its southern December solstice extreme.

The Bororo orient their most prominent and ritually significant structure—the *baimanagejewu* or "house in the center"—with its longer sides facing due east and west along their major village axis. In premodern times, specific Bororo clans were designated to locate and orient their villages, and did so by careful solar observations, among other considerations. This relationship is encoded in the Bororo social system with Meri, Sun, a member of one of these clans, located immediately adjacent to the village's east-west axis. Some Bororo today remain well aware of the northern and southern horizon extremes of the sun's annual movement and are close observers of the path of the sun, which they call *meri etawara*. The sun is still used for telling the time of day, especially through the simple but effective method of pointing the entire hand, palm down, to the sun's position. By doing this and stating *"Meri woe"* ("[When] the sun [is] here"), they can easily plan or coordinate an action for a specified time. The Bororo also have a well-developed concept of the zenith, which they call *baru oia*, "the center of the sky." (Unfortunately as far as Bororo zenith sun observations are concerned, in November and February when the sun is in their zenith, the sky is often under the heavy cloud cover of the rainy season, and I was unable to record any data specific to this phenomenon during my field study.)

The solar zenith passage was of considerable significance to the archaeologically and ethnohistorically known Mayas and Incas, for whom these phenomena played critical roles in cosmology and calendar (see for example, Aveni, 1989a, 1997; Zuidema, 1981b). The Maya of the Yucatan peninsula, for example, at least at the time of conquest, seemed to be using one of the sun's passages through the zenith (probably in mid-July) as their determinant of New Year (Aveni, 1989a:237). Significance of zenith passage continues into the ethnographic present. Aveni reports (from R. Girard) that among Maya in both Honduras and Guatemala, observation of the zenith sun is important in forecasting weather and activities pertinent to their agricultural cycle, and the "elaborate" rituals that accompany these solar events (1980:40). This correlates favorably with Barbara Tedlock's work among contemporary Maya, whom she reports using solar zenith passages "to fix dates in the agricultural calendar" (1999:44) and her interpretation of primary directional significance for the Maya as "east, zenith, west, nadir" (B. Tedlock, 1992:173). That tropical peoples interested in zenith sun passages (and other zenith phenomena) also should be interested in the nadir is logical. The *nadir* is the point diametrically opposite the zenith, beneath the observer. Of course, the obvious difficulty here is that no empirical observation of astronomical bodies actually passing through the nadir is possible for an earth-based observer. Discussion of nadir crossings is, therefore, essentially theoretical. (Attentive to this, Zuidema, 1981b, has employed the term *anti-zenith* in his analysis and discussion of nadir-related phenomena in his works on the Inca.)

In his work among Quechua-speaking natives (*runa*) in Misminay, Peru, Gary Urton (1981) found a number of references to zenith passage for calendrical purposes, but not only of the sun: a variety of celestial phenomena (e.g., specific stars and the Milky Way, covered in chapter 4) also were observed in association with a zenith crossing. In Misminay the sun is observed for decisions on when to plant, and in this somewhat complicated combination of astronomical observations, field research, intellectual inquiry, and deep context cultural meaning we find significance of both the zenith sun and its nadir passage. The growing season of maize in Misminay is from seven to eight months, but at its altitude the danger of frosts threaten crops planted either too early or too late. Planting, at least of the important maize crop, must therefore occur locally between August and October, a period of time the Misminay runa designate through solar observations as the "center-sun." This period of time is precisely bounded by the sun when it passes through the nadir at midnight in mid-August and through the zenith at noon at the end of October, dates associated with sunrise and sunset observations as seen from Misminay (Urton, 1981:69–77). As summarized by Urton, "the limits of the center-sun/planting-sun in Misminay are calculated fairly precisely to provide for the survival of crops . . . the limits of the 'center-sun' may correspond to the four points of the zenith and nadir sunrise and sunset" (76). Urton's work on these topics was stimulated by R. T. Zuidema's pioneering work on the calendrical significance of zenith and nadir passages of the sun (and moon) to the Inca (see e.g., Zuidema, 1981b), who were in political control of the area of Misminay at the time of the Spanish conquest.

THE MIDNIGHT SUN AND NIGHT AT MIDDAY

An observer above the Arctic Circle sees the sun move in flat planes around the sky. Not only does the sun never near the zenith, there will be times when it circles the sky without setting, and other times when it will not rise at all.

For the Inuit at Igloolik, Canada, at slightly less than 70° N, "the sun is below the horizon for forty-six days between 29 November and 14 January and above the horizon for sixty-six days between 19 May and 24 July" (U.S. Naval Observatory, as reported in MacDonald, 1998:11). The extended period of night is called Tauvikjuaq, "Great Darkness," and is associated with poor hunting and dangerous travel. During this fearful time extra supernatural protection was sought by the Inuit through ritual and the recitation of sacred words (MacDonald, 1998:101).

On the other hand, the return of the sun in mid-January (an occurrence affected by unpredictable effects of *refraction* of sunlight in the thick atmosphere near the horizon) was often met by the *Arctic* Inuit with "exuberant festivities" and new fire ceremonies, when all old lights would be put out and rekindled (MacDonald, 1998:107–10). It was also a time for making long-term weather forecasts, based on observations of the sun's reappearance vis-à-vis the first new moon of the year (111).

SOLAR ECLIPSES

A *solar eclipse* is the *conjunction* between the moon and sun, and so can occur only at the time of astronomical "new" moon or that time each synodical month (the month of lunar phases, discussed in chapter 3) when the moon is otherwise not visible to us. Since the moon as viewed from the Earth appears to be coincidentally the same diameter as the sun, a total solar eclipse can only occur with an exact alignment of the sun, moon, and Earth, and then will be visible from only a small portion of the Earth's surface. Solar eclipses, therefore, happen rarely for residents of any specific geographic area (although technically they occur more frequently than lunar eclipses [Aveni, 1980:78]). It is even rarer to have such an occurrence as observed by native peoples reported by a trained ethnographer. This is unfortunate, since the daylight darkening and nocturnal sensation produced by a total solar eclipse is quite sensational.

Meri bi or "death of Meri" is how the Bororo refer to an eclipse, and the Salesian missionaries report that it is cause for "great terror"

as it is perceived to foretell death and misfortune (Albisetti and Venturelli, 1962:791). A *bari* shaman, one of two types of religious specialists among the Bororo, will attempt to intercede with the spirits
believed to be causing the effect, as well as read the omen in its application to his village. The Timbira north of the Bororo interpret a solar
eclipse as a struggle between Sun and Moon, described in myth as two
primordial males who discover each other and exist in a competitive
relationship (Nimuendajú, 1946:233, 243–44). Apparently nothing
active is done by the Timbira when one occurs—which contrasts with
their reaction to a lunar eclipse (see chapter 3)—but anxious waiting.
Misfortune is also feared by the Maya during either solar or lunar
eclipse (B. Tedlock, 1992:184), but it is unclear if any specific behavior
is associated with the event.

In temperate North America, the Tewa of the U.S. Southwest
apparently dreaded a solar eclipse, deeming it a sign of displeasure of
their Sun Father with them, signaling his possible departure forever
from the sky. Their response was to devise a ceremony of propitiation
and prayer (Williamson, 1984:189). Also in the Southwest, the Navajo,
while calling a solar eclipse "death of the sun" like the Bororo, see less
dread in its occurrence. They believe it to be a sign of imbalance in the
energy transfer between Earth and sun, and while some ceremonial
observances may be made, in general the occurrence is considered
benign: the sun who has taken the energy of too many lives, now has to
give back, meaning fewer or no deaths immediately following the
eclipse (Pinxten and Van Dooren, 1992:103). Traditional Cherokee of
the Southeast perceive either solar or lunar eclipse as an attack on the
sun or moon by a great celestial frog, and would attempt to scare it
away with noise (Mooney, 1982 [1900]:257).

In the Arctic, the earliest accounts by non-natives in the area
describe the Inuit reacting with considerable apprehension to a solar
eclipse (MacDonald, 1998:136–38), although the full import of the event
in the indigenous thought systems was not wholly grasped or reported.
Such reactions have changed significantly, however, with increased contact and Western education in the area. (Other sun-related phenomena,
such as haloes and rainbows, are discussed in chapter 6.)

SOCIOCULTURAL SIGNIFICANCE OF THE SUN

Technical knowledge of the fundamental motion of the sun is basic
to fieldwork in ethnoastronomy. But of real interest to ethnoastronomers are the native observations themselves, and the cultural meaning
and use made of these observations. The Mescalero Apache in the U.S.
Southwest, for example, as observers in the north Temperate Zone, see

the sun rise in the east, climb up through the southern portion of the sky, then descend to the west, and therefore call "sunwise" all circular motion that proceeds from left to right (or "clockwise"). For them, it is the prescribed direction of movement for many ceremonial and even daily activities (Farrer, 1996:70). Likewise, the Plains Crow consider sunwise motion sacred, and use it to pattern their own movement in sacred space: "when one enters a tipi, a sweatlodge, a Sun Dance arbor, or any other sacred structure, one turns to the left and circles to the right" (McCleary, 1997:102), an attitude similar to that of the Lakota, as well (Black Elk in Neihardt, 1979 [1932]).

Certainly it is important for ethnoastronomers to study how non-Western peoples observe the sun, their use of these observations to plan their activities, and any cosmological significance ascribed to the solar entity. But it is also important to leave behind ethnocentric notions of the sun as an orb of intensely hot gases about which we on Earth revolve. Ethnoastronomers should also try to learn who/what the sun is, what meaning it holds for any given people. For the Bororo, the sun, meri, is clearly related to Sun, Meri, a culture "hero" present in much of their folklore. Meri as culture hero is characterized by such traits as strength, cleverness, and the ability to restore life, which he exercises on several occasions to bring his brother, Ari or Moon, back to life after several different mishaps kill him. In these attributes and through the kinship relationship between Sun and Moon, the Bororo are expressing metaphorically their conceptual understanding of the celestial sun and moon. That these cosmic brothers, who are also tricksters, are associated with heat is another, more overt link between the celestial and mythic entities. As described in the Bororo myth that begins this chapter, the pair is literally fanned by the Karawoe up into the sky after one mischievous prank too many: they have become "too hot" to be allowed to stay down on Earth! (Additional comments about the Meri-doge are presented in the next chapter; see Fabian, 1992, especially chapter 6, for more details of the sun and moon among the Bororo).

Trying to depict accurately what the sun is as a celestial body as understood from the Bororo perspective is difficult, especially due to the acculturating influences of their immersion—geographically, if less so socioculturally—within the nation-state of Brazil. Earlier accounts of the Salesians suggest that the Bororo perceived the sun as a shining gold disc that is carried through the sky by the spirits of a particular category of deceased shamans (Colbacchini and Albisetti, 1942:97). Very little was forthcoming from contemporary villagers about traditional concepts of what the sun is, substantiating my call for a living ethnoastronomy to learn what we can of native knowledge and beliefs while it is still there. For the Bororo, the sun is used in village orientation, for day-time reckoning and for planning and carrying out seasonal activities; its movement inspires the direction of social movement as mapped out on the village circle; and as an anthropomorphic culture hero it provides one model for personal character and social interactions (Fabian, 1992; 1994 [1995]).

The Ramkokamekra of the Eastern Timbira, residing only about 5° south of the equator, "regard themselves as primarily dependent on the Sun (Put) and in much lesser degree also on the Moon (Puduvri)" (Nimuendajú, 1946:232; orthography has been simplified). Addressed as either "Father" or "Grandfather," Sun may be supplicated for rain or to protect plants and animals, may be spontaneously addressed in private petition, and is asked to protect a newborn infant. But there seems little technical observing of the sun for calendrical purposes, and as Nimuendajú reported, "They do not ponder the nature of the solar body" (232).

North of the equator in Mesoamerica the Maya continue to observe the sun keenly, as did their Classic ancestors a millenium and a half ago. In the pre-Conquest Quiché Maya text, *Popol Vuh,* the culture hero Hunahpu with his brother Xbalanque, defeat the Lords of Death and the Underworld and ascend into the sky, where "the sun belongs to one and the moon to the other [respectively]" (D. Tedlock, 1996:141). Today, B. Tedlock reports that the Maya "describe the sun as a human or god-like figure with a brilliant round face, who rises each day on the eastern horizon and faces his universe with north on his right hand and south on his left hand" (1992:178). As was true in Classic times, the Maya today still observe the sun for calendrical and agricultural purposes, in combination with other astronomical observations.

In the U.S. Southwest among the Navajo, Sun is perceived as a deity of great power who together with their "most beloved deity," Changing Woman, procreate the Hero Twins, who were important in making the land habitable for humans by slaying monsters (Griffin-Pierce, 1992:30; Oswalt and Neely, 1999:341). But Sun, Jóhonaa'éí, is also a disk carried by He-Who-Returns-Carrying-One-Turquoise. While monthly and nocturnal time is marked by the moon, "The sun's movement along the horizon is responsible for the seasons" (Griffin-Pierce, 1992:74–75). Among the Puebloan neighbors of the Navajo the sun is described as "the most powerful deity in their large pantheon of gods" (Williamson, 1984:59), and is a dominant force in their lives. As such it is offered sacred cornmeal and prayer. In Hopi towns sun priests or watchers make use of detailed horizon observations for a solar calendar used to determine planting times and times for major ceremonies, clearly continuing an ages-old practice in the region encoded in ancient architecture, rock art, and folklore (Williamson 1984:ch. 5).

For the Cherokee of the Southeast the primordial sun was too hot, so conjurors raised the sky arch to be seven hand-breadths high so that the sun would be far enough to not burn everything (Mooney, 1982 [1900]:239). Mythically, Sun and Moon are described as sister and brother, respectively, who have an incestuous relationship (256–57), but the gender of the two is not always consistent in Cherokee lore (cf. 440, n. 7). The sun, called differently by commoners and priests, is also known as Unelanuh'hi, "the Great Apportioner" (259), indicating a significance derived from solar observation of order and organization.

Scant information can be found on concepts about or observations of the sun for far southern peoples. The Ona of Tierra del Fuego consider the male sun husband to the moon (Cooper, 1946:124), while further north in the southern temperate region of the Gran Chaco, Sun is commonly a woman and Moon a man, unless the two are male twins, when their relationship of stronger-weaker brothers is common and similar to that perceived by the Bororo (Métraux, 1946:366).

In the far north Yukon Territory the Kutchin observe sun and moon for weather prediction (detailed more in chapter 6), but Osgood (1936), who reports on the Kutchin in detail provides little other mention of sun or moon. Most commonly among the Arctic Inuit the sun and moon are considered to be sister and brother, respectively. Once human, they rise into the sky following brother Moon's incestuous advances on sister Sun. As she flees carrying burning moss, he pursues with the same burning material that eventually goes out; their chase carries them into the sky realm. The story is recounted in a myth that MacDonald (1998) describes as "one of the most widespread and complex of all Inuit traditions," an epic story "addressing universal concerns about creation, social and cosmic order, nourishment, retribution, and renewal" (97).

Clearly, the sun stands out as an entity of major proportions in much native astronomy, cosmology, and folklore. Recognized for its powerful presence and regular motion, it has been from the native perspective a force by and with which to reckon.

EXERCISES: SOLAR OBSERVATIONS

WARNING: NEVER LOOK DIRECTLY AT THE SUN! Doing so especially once the sun is above the filtering effects of the thicker atmosphere on the horizon can cause serious eye damage.

Exercise 2.1   Gnomons and shadow-casting

Needed: a straight stick or rod, some smaller objects as markers, and a tape measure; a flat unobstructed space, and sunny weather.

Objectives: to determine true north (and/or south), to get a sense of the sun's movement over time, and possibly to record a northern and/or southern extreme for the rising and/or setting sun.

A **gnomon** can be any device used to cast a shadow. We are interested in how a gnomon can be used to tell time and directionality.

Find a relatively flat space free of obstructing and shadow-casting features, such as a hill-top, field, courtyard, or even a flat roof. (Ideally, your chosen site can remain undisturbed for several weeks.) Stand your stick or rod, now a gnomon, in the center of your chosen space. On one day, try to establish actual noon, and true north, by measuring the length of the shadow at least once every five minutes as you approach the clock-time of noon.

How will you know when it is noon? What direction does the shadow mark at noon?

Record your findings (date, time, length of shadow) and mark the length of the noon line. Repeat this procedure on at least one other day and compare your results. (If you are on a semester schedule, try doing it twice each month.) What can you say about the sun at noon from your findings? If possible, try this every day for two weeks, one week on each side of the official solstice and/or equinox, and record your findings. Does the sun really "stand still" at the solstice? How does this contrast with its movement at the equinox?

If your space allows, use your gnomon to indicate the direction of sunrise and sunset, and compare this with sunrise/sunset measurements taken on other days. Report on your observations of the movement of the shadow.

Exercise 2.2   *Marking sunrise and sunset*

Needed: A flat space with unobstructed view of the horizon, and at least two sticks with smaller markers optional.

Objectives: To mark the sun's movement on the horizon.

Since looking at the orb of the sun is extremely hazardous to your eyes, wear sunglasses and try to catch the sun's first gleam on rising, and its last gleam as it sets. (Do NOT stare at the sun!) Pick a spot from which you can observe the horizon (even better if you have a view of both horizons from the same spot). Be sure to mark this space as the center of your "observatory." If you can work with a partner, have him/her hold one stick as a fore sight while you look over a stick placed at the center (this becomes the back sight). Have your partner place his/her stick vertically right where you see the gleam of the rising or setting sun. If you are working alone, use a stick at arm's length, and another just in front of you. Record the date and time. Once the line is fixed in place, take note of any distinguishing horizon features at the rise or set point, and record all of this. Make additional observations as frequently as practical, remembering to make each observation from your fixed "observatory" center point. Measure the distances between the markers established on different dates (sticks can be removed and replaced with smaller markers if desired). Analyze your data; what can you say about the movement of the sun as seen on the horizon? If possible, do exercise 2.2 for two weeks on either side of a solstice or equinox, and compare that with observations made at other times.

Endnote

[1] From Colbacchini and Albisetti, 1942:237–38; an English version is included in Wilbert and Simoneau, 1983:43–44.

Chapter Three

The Moon

The dry season night was crisp and clear, early enough in the season so that the smoky haze of Jorukau, the "season of fire" as the Bororo call it, was not yet a hindrance to celestial observance. It was late and the village lay mostly silent and asleep, with only muted rustlings and occasional muffled conversation as signs of life. From the village cattle herd scattered in the savanna beyond the village came quiet lowings, while from the grasses and brush all around came a veritable cacophony of night songs from insects and I knew not what other nocturnal creatures.

Sunset had occurred long enough ago that even the day's afterglow had left the western sky, and the deep indigo richness of the celestial vault lay fully exposed, moonless, sprinkled brilliantly with stars. We looked up at this wondrous expanse from our plaited palm mats, silent now after a session of speaking about specific objects visible overhead. My companion was a village elder of the Paiwoe clan, highly knowledgeable of traditional practices and lore. He lay there silently, taking a drag on his cigarette, hand-made with tobacco I had supplied, and blowing its rich aroma into the buggy air, where its smell mixed not unpleasantly with that of the smoldering palm stem we had near us in an effort to disinterest airborne pests.

"And what of *ari*, the moon?" I inquired after a long lapse into silence.

He puffed again on the cigarette, then hawked deeply to clear his throat and spat before replying.

"No moon tonight. Ari will rise in the west."

"In the west? Don't you mean rise in the east?"

"No, ari rises in the west."

There was little more productive conversation that night before we went off to our respective houses. I was perplexed, my curiosity piqued by his assertion that the moon "rose" in the west, when my own observational background and knowledge of astronomy assured me that the moon, as with the sun and stars, rose in the east then set in the west.

The next evening, just after sunset, we two were again together. Looking westward the elder motioned to where the slimmest white curve of the moon's new crescent could be seen above the western horizon.

"You see?" he said to me, as if helping a child to understand, "*Ari rutu*, ari rises in the west."

SYNODICAL PERIOD

The single most noteworthy regular feature of the night sky is the moon, second only to the sun in brightness, and at its full phase coincidentally equal in size with the orb of the sun for Earth-based observers. So dramatic and fundamental is the moon's nocturnal presence that a sun/day and moon/night opposition is a common crosscultural conceptualization. (While the moon is admittedly outshone by the sun during the day, few people today seem to be aware of the moon's daytime presence during significant portions of each month.) For peoples with less restriction on their observations of the sky than our contemporary urban lifestyle permits, the moon and its interplay with the sun are of great interest, serving as the basis for calendars and myriad myths of culture heroes and the meaningful relationships between these oft-anthropomorphized entities.

A large part of what makes the moon such a dramatic and observed presence in the (especially) night sky is its changing shape, its phases. Termed its synodic or **synodical period** from the Latin and Greek roots of synodus/sunodus, "meeting (the sun)," the moon's period of phases results from its position relative to the sun for Earth-based observers, punctuated monthly by its "meeting" or conjunction with the sun and consequent disappearance from view for one or two days/nights, the technically astronomical "new moon." For most lay and native observers, the new moon is the first reappearance of the moon after its disappearance. At this time the moon is a thin sliver near the western horizon, visible shortly after sundown and soon thereafter itself sinking below the horizon. Over the course of the next 29.5 days (its formal synodical period), the moon will appear higher in the sky at sunset and wax until it rises full, opposite the setting sun about halfway through this period, after which it will rise later and wane until its next "meeting" with the sun.

(a)

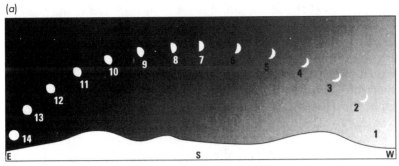

Moon on successive days, looking west after sunset

(b)

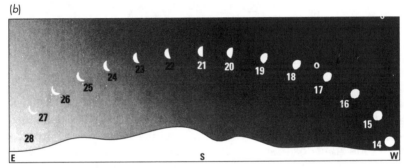

Moon on successive days, looking east before sunrise

Figure 2. The many faces of the moon. In about a month the moon moves eastward among the stars all the way around the sky, passing through all its phases as it goes. (a) On days 1 to 14, the observer looks to the south after sunset and sees the moon wax from first visible crescent to full phase. (b) On days 14 to 28, the observer watches the southern sky before sunrise and witnesses the moon wane from full to last crescent. Gone for a day or two, the moon finally returns to position 1.

This phenomenon of the moon's reappearance low in the west, followed by its higher and fuller manifestation on subsequent evenings, apparently accounts for the Paiwoe elder's assertion that the "moon rises in the west." It would have been easy to discount my *informant's* statement about moonrise in the west as ignorance on his part of the technicalities of lunar motion. But sensitivity to the native perspective is paramount in ethnographic research, with the need to control culturally biased assumptions extremely important, as this example shows. While counterintuitive to my Western mind, the Bororo perspective of the moon does have a practical efficacy in describing its synodical motion. Furthermore, this description of the moon's motion/position is relevant to and strengthens the various culturally perceived oppositional qualities of the moon-sun dyad: the moon, prominent at night, rises in the west at sunset, in contrast to the eastern sunrise of the day-prominent sun (further discussion of the opposition of sun and moon occurs below).

So fundamental and regular a marker of time have been the lunar phases that calendars for large-scale societies and civilizations were developed around them. Some of these calendars, such as among the Jewish and Muslim peoples, have been in use for centuries and even millennia. The English term "month" itself carries with it the historical significance of the moon's periodicity in dividing the year, even though the current Gregorian calendar's months are reckoned without relevance to the moon.

SIDEREAL PERIOD

Although the phases of the moon and its synodical period may be the most obvious lunar phenomena, another lunar periodicity deserves mention: that of the moon's position with respect to the stars, its *sidereal period*. This is about 27.33 days, making it somewhat problematic for consistent observations. However, the significance of the moon's position with respect to the stars as seen in the zodiacal houses in Western astrology hearkens to a historical interest in lunar sidereal positioning. Outside of the West, the ancient Chinese seem to have been focusing on this lunar period in their system of 28 constellations along the celestial equator. These star groups were a basis for a division of the sky into 28 segments considered "stewards" of the moon, and in which the moon was housed, one per day (Aveni, 1989:314–22). Sidereal lunar observations also seem to be important among contemporary Quiché Maya, who reckon an 82-day (27.33 x 3 = 81.99 rounded to 82) ritual period, apparently derived from moon and star observations (B. Tedlock, 1992:191).

In the Americas, Zuidema (1982) has argued convincingly for a sidereal lunar calendar of the Incas. His argument is based on ethnohistoric and other evidence that gives prominence to a calendric period of 328 days, a sort of sidereal "year" (27.33 x 12 = 327.96 rounded to 328) which, although not measuring 12 distinct sidereal lunations, nevertheless does incorporate paired and other sidereal periods. Some contemporary support for this scheme can be extrapolated from the work of Urton (1981) in Misminay, where he found that astronomical observations by Quechua women significantly combine lunar and stellar associations (79). The relative paucity of ethnographic information on sidereal lunar observations may be due to multiple factors, such as receptivity of the ethnographer or

even gender-sensitive knowledge (cf. Urton, 1981:79) for limitations of a
male ethnographer with respect to female lunar knowledge).

CALENDRICAL INTERMESHING OF MOON AND SUN: INTERCALATION

What are the implications of these different lunar periodicities
and their application in a formal calendric system, one that is to be useful year after year? Many native systems count time periods in
"moons," as in fact does the Western Gregorian calendar with its twelve
months (from Old English mona, moon, and monao, month, through
Middle English moone and moneth). The Bororo may once have reckoned a period of ten named months (Fabian, 1992:98–99), but pragmat-
ically today for time reckoning refer less to any specific moon count as
to seasonal and other indicators of time passage, or simply the dates on
a contemporary Brazilian calendar. With the heavy influence of our
modern calendar system on indigenous time reckoning, many peoples
have left off reckoning in their indigenous systems and have adopted
the twelve named months of the Gregorian year.

Records of named month systems do exist, however, although
these often are listed in a way as to connect a specific set of twelve
native months with January through December. For example, Osgood's
report on the arctic/subarctic Kutchin includes such a list, the indigenous terms translated as an "outstanding characteristic of the month,"
such as January, *no tco tson:* "Month when the days grow longer," or
July, *vo nan yi da tcox:* "Month of moulting feathers" (1936:98; I have
simplified some of his orthography). Similarly descriptive month
names are used by Black Elk of the Lakota in his autobiographical
recounting, such as "Moon When the Cherries Turn Black" (August) or
"Moon When the Plums Are Scarlet" (September; as reported by
Neihardt, 1979 [1932]), and demonstrate the significance of lunar
observations for attending to practical cultural concerns.

The problem with such systems is that the solar or tropical year
by which we reckon our Gregorian calendar is approximately 365.24
days long, a number simply irreconcilable in any facile way with the
lunar synodical ($12 \times 29.5 = 354$, some eleven days short) or sidereal ($13
\times 27.3 = 354.9$, ten days short) periods. This becomes a classic and
recurring problem in premodern world calendar systems: the obvious
lunar phases, which serve nicely to delineate time on a monthly scale,
will quickly get out of synchrony with seasonal time responsive to the
annual solar cycle. One solution, as adopted by the Muslims in their
Hijri calendar, has been to reckon ritual time by the moon exclusive of
the solar year, with months alternating between 29 and 30 days. In this

system, the well-known month of fasting, Ramadan, occurs in different seasons over a 30-year cycle (Westrheim 1993, chapter 8).

Another solution, intended to keep the lunar and solar cycles in greater synchrony, is by *intercalation*, the insertion of an extra time period into the calendar. In the Hebrew or Jewish calendar, for example, years are reckoned by counting either 12 or 13 lunations (of 29 or 30 days) in any specific year in order to keep the synodical months seasonally synchronized. In its 19-year cycle, the Hebrew calendar adds an extra thirteenth *intercalary month* in the third, sixth, eighth, eleventh, fourteenth, seventeenth, and nineteenth years (Westrheim, 1993, chapter 5).

A native North American calendar that appears to make an effort to synchronize moons with the solar year was recorded by Boas among the Central Eskimo in the 1880s. Normally naming thirteen months, "every few years" they would leave out the month called *siringilang* ("without sun"), applied to that time of year (in the Arctic) "when the sun does not rise and there is scarcely any dawn. Thus every few years this month is totally omitted, when the new moon and the winter solstice coincide" (Boas, 1888:644–48). This might be an example of a "negative" intercalation, where a period is removed from, rather than inserted into, a calendar. Obviously, it remains difficult to integrate lunar and solar/seasonal periodicities in a single formalized calendar. Our own Gregorian calendar has long left off trying, and many modern wall calendars leave off completely any lunar phase information.

LUNAR ECLIPSES

As already described earlier in this chapter, a full moon rises diametrically opposite the setting sun. Sun, Earth, and moon achieve this celestial alignment once every 29.5 days in accord with the moon's synodical cycle. But while the moon reflects back toward us the sun's bright light, Earth's shadow is cast outward into space towards the moon. When the moon passes through our shadow during its full phase, we may observe a *lunar eclipse*.

Although a lunar eclipse may not be quite as awesome as the daylight darkening and night-arousal of a total solar eclipse, a total lunar eclipse is still an impressive occurrence; under certain conditions, such as on a snow-blanketed winter night as I recently witnessed it, it indeed can be a spectacular event. A lunar eclipse begins with a darkening of an edge or section of the moon, which can be dramatic enough to appear as if some cosmic creature had taken a bite out of it! Gradually, over the course of the next hour, this blackness will creep up the surface of the moon until only a gleaming sliver of light remains. But once that light is also snuffed out, the moon appears like a shadowy apparition of its former full self, although not a colorless or gray ghost. Rather, it takes on earth tones, from a dark brown at the edge furthest from where the moon's last gleam shone, through a dull orange in its middle, to perhaps pale ochre at its recently brilliant edge. This process more or less reverses itself as time goes by, the whole phenomenon lasting up to several hours.

For anyone who has camped or lived away from the structures and artificial lights of our modern environment, few other regular natural phenomena can compare with the full moon as an impressive display, and one that radically can affect behavior patterns. Certainly the Bororo occasionally took advantage of the full moon to extend daytime activities, echoing our Western concept of the "harvest moon" of autumn. But the full moon can also be used for special circumstances and celebrations, such as marking the beginning of the important Jewish festival of Pesach or Passover (15–22 Nisan in the Hebrew calendar), or the opening of religiously significant Sun Dance bundles in "Full Moon Meetings" among the Crow Indians (McCleary, 1997:103).

Considering the significance of the full moon in many cultures, imagine the surprise and wonder, the concern, even the fear experienced as a portion of the moon begins to disappear, as its nocturnal glow is snuffed out and darkness reclaims the night.

Called ari bi, "moon's death" in Bororo, such an eclipse is reportedly met with "terror" and dread, as it is believed to foretell dire misfortune. A bari shaman who intercedes with certain types of spirits will try to intercede and prognosticate during such an occurrence (Albisetti and Venturelli, 1962:92). Among the Timbira the event is similarly called "dying of the moon." Nimuendajú (1946) describes a lunar eclipse he experienced in a village and the consternation it caused; the complicated response of the natives included lighting large fires, singing and dancing, shooting incendiary arrows, and even the "offering" of two young girls for the moon to "take" (233).

North of the equator, the Maya also consider a lunar eclipse dangerous and do not look directly at it. Pregnant women must take special care not to bathe in a natural waterway during a lunar eclipse for fear of a stillborn or deformed baby. In general the event signals famine and sickness, and is met in some communities "by a great outcry, shouting and banging on tables, beating on drums and pots and pans, ringing the church bells, shooting off firecrackers or guns, and lighting great bonfires" (B. Tedlock, 1992:184). Far north in the Arctic, many Inuit peoples historically met lunar eclipses with the same dread with which they met a solar eclipse, associating both with various ill effects. Danger from such phenomena was sometimes perceived as gender-specific, stemming from the attributed sex of the astronomical entity (to the Inuit, Moon is male) to members of the opposite human sex (MacDonald, 1998:136–40).

Perhaps some of the fear, often responded to by noise as among traditional Cherokee or tribes of the Gran Chaco in South America (e.g., the Toba and Abipón), is due to the perception of the moon being eaten by some cosmic creature. For the Cherokee this is a giant frog in the sky, and the great noise made is said to frighten the beast away (Mooney, 1982 [1900]:257); among the Gran Chaco peoples it is a celestial jaguar (Métraux, 1946:366). However the phenomenon is explained, as with a solar eclipse, a lunar eclipse is generally disturbing to most native peoples. As McCleary (1997) comments, "The sun and moon are constant and move in concert with each other. It is understandable that a break in that constant, seemingly predictable movement—such as with an eclipse—causes discomfort" (102).

CROSSCULTURAL SIGNIFICANCE OF THE MOON

Ari, Moon, and Meri, Sun—the Meri-doge—are mythically prominent Bororo culture heroes that are seldom separated. This celestial pairing is basic to many systems of astronomy, emphasizing the perceived relationship of these celestial entities, a relationship that is frequently expressed in mythic prose. The fact that the same Bororo words, *meri* and *ari*, are used to refer to both the celestial entities as well as the brothers of folklore, indicates the metaphorical identifying of celestial bodies with culture heroes. Pertinent characteristics expressive of this metaphorical relationship include the following:

Folkloric Meri-doge	Celestial Sun and Moon
Strength of Meri relative to younger brother Ari	Power of sun to similar-sized but weaker moon
Meri gains control over night	Sunrise ends nighttime
Travels of Meri-doge marked by significant features of terrain	Horizon observations made of sun and moon in their annual and monthly cycles
Several stories of the deaths of Ari and his resuscitation by Meri	Monthly disappearances of the moon, or lunar eclipses, and the moon's reappearance
The Meri-doge are fanned into the sky for being too hot to stay on Earth	Heat of the tropical sun

Among the Eastern Timbira north of the Bororo, similar adventures and characteristics to those of Bororo folklore are described for the primal, male Sun and Moon, although they share no stated blood bond there (Nimuendajú, 1946:243–45).

Crossculturally, the nature of the relationship between sun and moon, and even their gender, is different. Among Quechua-speaking

Indians, for example, the sun is perceived as male and the moon female; correspondingly, male runa tend to emphasize solar observations, while female runa observe and relate more to the moon. (Urton, 1981, chapter 3). In contrast, Cherokee folklore depicts the sun as female and the moon as male in a sibling relationship that becomes incestuous when the moon mates with his sister at night. Wishing to know her seductor, whom she cannot see, Sun puts ashes on her hands which the next day shame her brother Moon by this identification. It is Moon's shame for this affair that makes him "thin as a ribbon" as Sun draws near each month (Mooney, 1982 [1900]:256–57). As already mentioned in the previous chapter, the Arctic Inuit have a strikingly similar story to that of the Cherokee, where male Moon is again the aggressor in his relationship with his sister, Sun. Both carry torches as Moon chases Sun across the sky, but Moon's torch burns out (Mary-Rousselière, 1984:441; Boas, 1888:597; MacDonald, 1998:97–98).

Menil, Moon, has special significance for women among the traditional Cahuilla of California, where she is honored as the only female among the earliest beings, the mother of all Cahuilla, and a great culture heroine. Moon is credited with teaching people how to enjoy themselves (at least in part through specific songs, dances, and games) and their world; with establishing the social order and ritual; with providing moral instruction on the right way to live; and even with how to enter heaven after death (Bean, 1992:165–69). She is particularly associated with the menstrual cycle and special instruction for girls and women relevant to menstruation and pregnancy. As one Cahuilla woman put it, "you gauge your period by the phases of the moon. When it doesn't follow that way, the person hasn't taken care of themselves" (174). Again we see here the use of astronomical knowledge as guidelines for proper living, patterns in the sky matched to living patterns on the ground.

Clearly, all of these stories attempt to express in human qualities and terms some of the observed solar and lunar characteristics and their interrelationship in the sky.

While it may be logical (as happens among the runa in the Andes and among the Cahuilla) to associate the moon with women due in part to the menstrual cycle and its comparability to the mean of lunar synodical and sidereal periods, data from the other cultures cited above indicate that this need not coordinate with an anthropomorphized *female* moon. Ironically in everyday usage, Bororo speak of a woman's *lua* (Portuguese) or "moon" to indicate her menstrual period, although indigenously *ari* or moon is associated with the male culture hero Ari; this suggests a borrowed Brazilian concept.

Of course, observations of the moon are significant in their own right. Among the Bororo, the synodical lunar period is used to punctuate the flow of annual time, while the moon's position in the night sky is used to reckon the passing of nighttime. Observations of lunar phases and positioning are used in numerous ways, for example as indicators for collecting the several all-important palm species used to craft numerous traditional cultural items or for when to plant varieties of domestic produce. The angle and fullness of the first reappearing crescent of the new moon is also used as an indicator of upcoming weather or human fortune (see Fabian, 1992:92–96; Blatt-Fabian, 1985).

In the tropics north of the equator, Maya farmers also carefully observe lunar phases, using these observations as factors in determining such activities as butchering, harvesting, woodcutting, planting, and sexual intercourse (B. Tedlock, 1992:185). Further north among the Crow Indians of the temperate Plains, during the new or full moon is the appropriate time to open sacred Medicine bundles, while its orientation as a new crescent, similarly as among the Bororo, is used as a prognosticator of weather and human fortune (McCleary, 1997:103–5).

Aside from its relationship with the sun, the moon holds its own "preeminent place in Inuit astronomy" (MacDonald, 1998:132). Its phases were used as a measure of time; its presence and light, sometimes circumpolar during winter's "great darkness," is greatly appreciated; and it is recognized as influencing ocean tides and currents and women's menstrual cycles, as well as the movement of land and sea animals (132). The moon or Moon-man is also important indigenously as a source of fertility, an aid for hunting, and a helper of abused and childless women and orphans (133–35). In general, power and help from Moon was accessed by shamans "who frequently visited [Moon] on a wide range of altruistic errands calculated to benefit their people in one way or another" (134).

Overall, the moon is one of the most significant celestial entities in native astronomies, often heavily imbued with symbolic significance. It is used for calendric purposes as well as for imparting messages important to successful adaptation and life in a specific region and culture. It is also one of the most rewarding celestial features to observe regularly.

EXERCISES: LUNAR OBSERVATIONS

Exercise 3.1   The "new moon": where, when, and what

Technically in Western astronomical parlance, the new moon occurs when, after waning and drawing closer to the sun, the moon disappears in the sun's glow. But for the practical native or layperson, or indeed for the religious specialist watching for the moment from when to begin counting the next synodical month, the "new moon" is literally the reappearance of the moon after it vanishes.

Begin observing the moon over the course of a month. At what time of day or night does the first sliver of the new moon appear?

Where is it with respect to the sun? With respect to the horizon? How is it shaped, and what is its angle? If possible, make and record observations of two or more newly appearing crescent moons and compare your data.

Exercise 3.2   Full moon: opposite the sun

When is the moon actually full? Can you determine an exact time through naked eye observations? How long does the moon actually appear full? This occurs how many days since the new moon? When and where is it in the sky when it appears full? What is its relationship to the sun? To the horizon?

Exercise 3.3   Lunar shadow casting

Obviously, the full moon is bright enough to cast shadows. If you have an observatory marked out on the ground for marking solar shadow casting, try using this same space for marking lunar shadows at full moon. Mark the direction of the shadow at moonrise and moonset and compare these with your solar marks. If possible, mark the moon's shadow when it is its shortest, that is, when it crosses the meridian. At what time of night does this occur? What direction is the shadow? How does this compare with your solar markings? Try to observe and mark the shadows of at least two full moons and compare your data.

Exercise 3.4   Lunar phases and positions in daytime and nighttime

Over the course of one or two (or more, if possible!) months, be attentive to the phase and position of the moon throughout the night and day. Although you know that the moon's synodical cycle is 29.5 days, what can you actually observe of the moon's cycle in that time? Of basic interest, and relevant to this "synodical" or sun-meeting cycle of the moon, is its position relative to the sun. The new- and full-moon positions have already been observed (exercises 3.1 and 3.2, respectively); what about first quarter (the waxing half moon) and third quarter (waning half moon) phases? Are these visible at sunrise or sunset? At midnight or midday? Where are they with respect to the horizon? Although rendered less significant by comparison with the sun, the moon is visible during the day, as well as the night. When during the synodical cycle are both the sun and moon in the sky together? When is the moon out at night?

The chart on the following page may be used to express some basic relationships of sun and moon, horizon or meridian, and day/nighttime. Record your observations either on a spontaneous basis, or during a specific position of the sun (e.g., sunset) or moon (e.g., meridian). By the time you finish this exercise, you should have a better understanding of how the Bororo Indians can say "The moon rises in the west."

Lunar Phase	Moon's Position	Sun's Position
New crescent moon		
Waxing (first quarter) moon		
Full moon		
Waning (third quarter) moon		
No (astronomical "new") moon		

Chapter Four

The Stars

Once in the past during the dry season when the men were off hunting and fishing and corn should have been growing, the women went to their gardens but returned empty-handed every day, to the disappointment of their children. A pesky child was finally allowed to join his mother in the cornfield, where to his surprise he found much corn being prepared and eaten by the women. Again that day the women returned with nothing, but the clever boy had hidden some corn in the hollow shafts of his arrows. The next day after the women had left, he shared this food with the other children.

"This is what our mothers do," he said. "They have a lot of corn, but they say they don't have any. They don't like us. What are we going to do? Where can we go to get away from our mothers?"

Deciding to run away up into the sky, the children had Hummingbird fly up with a line, which he fastened to a strong celestial *sucupira* tree. Up this line the children began their climb, the bigger ones helping and carrying their smaller siblings. Before they were able to climb out of sight, however, their mothers returned to the village.

"Where are the children?" the mothers said. They called: "Children, we're here!"

Seeing the children up in the sky, they tried to coax them back. "Come here, children," they called, and motioned with their breasts. "Come here and suck."

The children kept climbing, so the women started to climb up after them. As the children reached the end of the line, they could see their mothers emerging from the forest, climbing higher. Then the last boy cut the line, and the women fell, some onto trees, others onto the ground. Where they fell, they turned into game animals.

As my elder Paiwoe informant finished sharing with me his version of this (condensed) Bororo story, he commented: "The women became beasts. The children became something beautiful in the sky. Because of this there are stars in the sky."[1]

For those of us who spend much of our nighttime in bed, the stars remain relatively unknown; although stars are present in the daytime, the sun's much brighter luminance renders them invisible to the naked human eye. For those of us with an active nightlife in a bustling modern city, the glare of street lamps and neon lights and the dominant height of urban architecture rising from smog-clouded streets preclude any quality stargazing. For those of us with TVs, VCRs, computers, and other visually stimulating devices, there is little interest in watching the stars since there are so many other sights to entertain us. For those of us with clocks, calendars, detailed date books and planners, there seems little point in making careful and consistent stellar observations: what we do when is coordinated with formal and standardized time measurement, removing us from the fundamental astronomical observations serving people in other times and places.

For many peoples throughout the world outside of the contexts described above, careful and interested stargazing has been and is of vital importance. For Earth-based observers, the multitude of visible stars exhibit the following important features:

1. They exist in patterns (individual stars are commonly grouped into culturally specific constellations);

2. They are arranged in a continuous sequence (stars are fixed in an order, so that, for example, Gemini is followed by Cancer and Leo); and

3. They move in ordered regularity (the stars you observe rising tonight after sunset will rise about four minutes earlier every night, until one year from now you will see the same stars rising at the same time).

These qualities allow people to use stars for time reckoning and temporal planning during a specific night, month, season, or year; as a medium, much like an artist's canvass, onto which culturally significant images may be projected; and as models or for guidance in culturally relevant ways.

THE CELESTIAL POLES, CELESTIAL EQUATOR, AND ECLIPTIC

As mentioned in chapter 1, due to the Earth's daily rotation, the stars appear to rise, set, and/or circle overhead around a fixed point in the sky. However, because the Earth actually "wobbles" in its rotation on its axis, over long periods of time the apparently fixed point will change. This rotational wobble and periodic shifting of the celestial poles among the stars is called *precession*.

To elaborate, modern Western astronomy imagines this apparently fixed point in the sky as an extension of the Earth's axis, so that just as there is a north (terrestrial) pole in the northern hemisphere, so there is a north celestial pole for northern latitude observers. Likewise, the south celestial pole is the south (terrestrial) pole's extension for observers in the southern hemisphere (observers precisely on the equator may have difficulty observing either pole due to local horizon elevations and atmospheric distortions).

Observers in the northern hemisphere are currently fortunate in having a single fairly bright star marking the pole: Polaris (North Star) in the constellation of Ursa Minor (Little Dipper). Throughout the course of the night, Polaris will appear to be fixed in place, in stark contrast to every other moving star. In the southern hemisphere, observers lack such a handy fixed marker; commonly the Southern Cross (the four brightest stars of the constellation Crucis) helps orient observers to the south celestial pole, but it is approximately 30° of arc distant from the actual pole.

Also, as already mentioned, the altitude of the celestial pole in either hemisphere is not at any arbitrary altitude, but rather is located at an altitude equivalent to the latitude of the observer. This means that the Bororo at about 15° south latitude (S) see their celestial pole about 15° above the southern horizon, while for me, currently residing outside of Chicago at about 43° N, the pole star is about halfway up above the northern horizon. As with discussions of solar and lunar observations, the latitude of the observer is of primary significance in determining the appearance of observable celestial phenomena.

The concept of the celestial equator was also mentioned in chapter 1. Imagining a single equatorial plane encircling the extent of the cosmos beyond our planet may be less than satisfying to some. But it is a helpful concept in providing an ease of the understanding of basic celestial motion as perceived from the Earth. Western astronomy projects the concept of a sphere from our Earth into visible outer space, so just as the terrestrial poles are extended in the *celestial sphere*, so is an equatorial circle or plane located halfway (90°) from either pole. The plane of the celestial equator is perpendicular to the axis or line connecting the poles on which the Earth rotates, and it intersects with the horizon at the cardinal east and west points. Due to the Earth's daily rotation on its axis, we see celestial objects rise and set, and they do so in lines that run along or parallel to the celestial equator.

So, for the Bororo at about 15° S, the south celestial pole will have an altitude of 15° above the southern horizon and the celestial equator will therefore intersect the meridian (the imaginary line overhead connecting north-south cardinal points) at 15° to the north of zenith, or at an altitude of 75° above the northern horizon. By hand measurements, this is only about one and one-half hands' width from the zenith (or a full seven and one-half hands' width from the plane of the idealized flat horizon). Since all celestial objects on a 24-hour basis will prescribe arcs along or parallel to this equatorial plane, you should be able to envision the significant verticality of celestial motion in the Tropics: objects really do appear to rise almost straight up, and set straight down. Compare this image with the sky as observed from the mid-temperate latitude of 40° N. Here the north celestial pole is 40° above the northern horizon, and therefore the celestial equator intersects the meridian at an altitude of 50° from the southern horizon, only about five hands' width up. Daily paths of astronomical motion here will be much more diagonal or slanting than at tropical latitudes.

I have stressed, above, daily paths of celestial motion of objects that lay on or move parallel to the celestial equator. For individual stars in any human lifetime this is a constant (although over longer periods of time their apparent paths will also change). However, the qualification is important for the movements of the sun, moon, and visible planets. On any specific day/night these entities will be seen to move in lines parallel to the celestial equator. However, unlike the relatively fixed or stable stars, the sun, moon, and planets do move; especially noticeable is the moon's shift in position every month and the sun's yearly swing from northern to southern extremes and back again. Movement off of the celestial equator is not totally random, however.

As described in chapter 1, the sun's apparent motion between northern and southern extremes over the course of the year is caused by the current 23½° tilt of the Earth's axis of rotation from its plane of revolution about the sun. Of course, the precessional wobble of the Earth also affects the tilt of its axis up to several degrees. Functionally, at its northern extreme (in June) the sun currently appears to move 23½° north of the celestial equator, and at its southern extreme (in December) is the same angular distance south of it. The apparent annual path of the sun in the heavens, which intersects with but is at a 23½° angle with the celestial equator, is called the ecliptic. It is marked among the stars by the Western constellations of the zodiac (discussed below). While the moon varies up to a further 5° from the sun's ecliptic line, and the planets also have slight variations due to their orbital planes, nevertheless all of these objects course along or near the ecliptic.

MAJOR STARS AND CONSTELLATIONS

As should be apparent by now, what is seen in the sky is filtered through an interpretive process of specific cultural lenses. When discussing major stars, we should be able to say that the brighter the star, the more obvious it is and therefore the more importance it has for naked eye observers. This may be true of the brightest (technically, the lowest magnitude) stars, but after considering brightness, we must be aware of the role of other variables in determining the importance of a specific star. Unfortunately, the nature and scope of this work preclude detailed observational guides for all major stars and constellations (guides that are readily available in other works), especially when taking into account all possible latitudes of observation. This section will provide only a basic introduction to this topic, an introduction that will include specific observations made by various peoples in the comparative section that follows.

It is difficult to discuss individual stars without reference to their *constellations*. Modern Western astronomy has organized the entire starry sky into 88 formal constellations, so that every star can be identified accurately and located, generally by Latin names for the constellations and a Greek letter for the star. The earlier the letter is in the Greek alphabet, generally the brighter the star relative to others in that constellation, so that the alpha (α) star is almost always the brightest. When using this technical system of identification, the possessive form of the Latin name follows the Greek letter; for example α Canis Majoris, which we also call Sirius, is the brightest star in the "Great Dog" constellation of Canis Major (and incidentally, *the* brightest star in the sky). Unfortunately for the average stargazer, however, such formal designations may be too much to process, and the use of "official" designations in addition to individualized or colloquial terms can be confusing. Furthermore, some common constellations, such as the Big Dipper in the north, actually are not constellations at all in the formal system. Such common groupings of stars that are usually only a part of a larger formal constellation are technically known as *asterisms* in Western astronomy. In fact, some asterisms, such as the Big Dipper, are probably the most recognizable groupings of stars in the sky to the average observer.

Observers precisely on the equator will have virtually the entire panoply of stars, asterisms, and constellations appearing at some time of the night over the course of a year (although weather conditions, high horizon altitudes, and/or atmospheric distortions may preclude this). Most temperate observers can see much of the sky progressively during the course of the night and seasons, but will miss some stars furthest from their celestial pole. For example, for an observer at 40° N, the lowest 40° of the southern sky will remain out of sight. By the time we cross the Arctic Circle, little more than half the stars potentially seen by someone on the equator will be visible, and if someone were to observe precisely from the North Pole, only the northern celestial hemisphere of stars will be visible (but all of them in one night!).

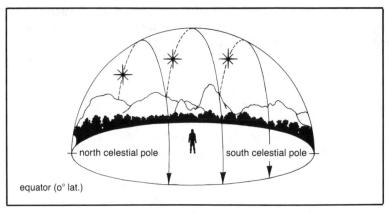

north celestial pole | south celestial pole

equator (o° lat.)

a

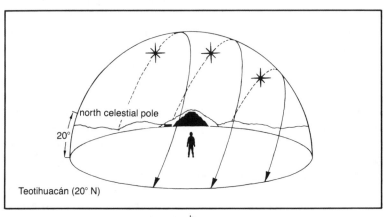

north celestial pole

20°

Teotihuacán (20° N)

b

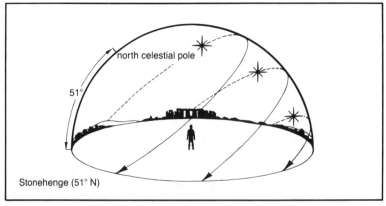

north celestial pole

51°

Stonehenge (51° N)

c

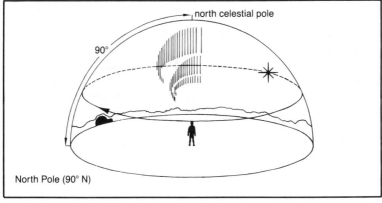

North Pole (90° N)

d

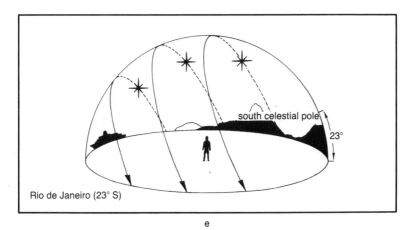

Rio de Janeiro (23° S)

e

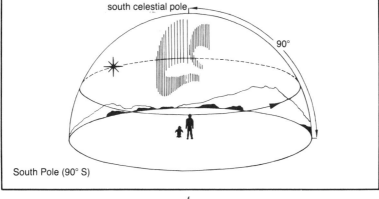

South Pole (90° S)

f

Figure 3. As these scenes depict, the stars appear to take very different paths for observers at different latitudes. The position of the fixed Pole Star (marked "north celestial pole" in the northern hemisphere) and the position of the south celestial pole on the sky also change. The altitude of the celestial pole is the same as the latitude of the observer.

Observers in temperate or more extreme latitudes away from the equator will be able to see some stars above the horizon all night every night all year round. Such stars or constellations are known as *circumpolar stars*, since they trace circles around the celestial pole. For an observer at about 40° N, the Big and Little Dippers are circumpolar, always in the sky, every night. This, of course, contributes to their significance in the northern latitudes, especially with their proximity to Polaris (α Ursae Minoris), the North Star at the north celestial pole, actually the outermost star in the handle of the Little Dipper. For tropical observers up to 15° or even 20° S where the Bororo are located, there are essentially no bright stars that fulfill this criterion, and so the concept of circumpolarity is essentially nonapplicable in their case.

The brightest star in the sky, as mentioned above, is Sirius (α Canis Majoris), also called the Dog Star in the West coincident with its location in the Great Dog constellation. For northern observers it is prominent but low in the southern sky in winter, a fitting season for it with its cold blue-white color. It is preceded by other noteworthy entities also prominent in fall and winter: the three lined-up stars that point to Sirius in the Belt of Orion (known as the Tres [three] Marias in Latin America), and their companions (north and south, respectively) red Betelgeuse and blue Rigel (α and β Orionis, respectively); about an hour ahead of Orion's Belt come Aldebaran (α Tauri) and the V-shaped Hyades (an asterism in the constellation Taurus); and about one hour in front of these is possibly the most famous asterism of all, the Pleiades. Orion's Belt is noteworthy as it sits essentially on the celestial equator, which means that it is visible to virtually every stargazer and it rises almost exactly due east and sets due west.

High overhead in the summer sky and prominent to northern observers is the Summer Triangle, comprised by Altair (α Aquilae) to the south, Vega (α Lyrae) the earliest aloft and so commonly more toward the west, and Deneb (α Cygni). Prominent in autumn and opposite to and half a sky away from the bowl of the Big Dipper is the large Square of Pegasus. A prominent spring star is Arcturus (α Boötis), locatable by extending the arc of the Big Dipper's handle away from its bowl. (For an enlightening and entertaining guide to seasonal astronomical phenomena, see Berman, 1995.)

While some of the above samples are prominent to southern observers as well as northern ones, other stars have importance in southern systems. The most commonly important stars are those in the Southern Cross and their near neighbors just behind them, α and β Centauri, circumpolar in southern Temperate Zones, and helping to define the general location of the south celestial pole. Red Antares (α Scorpii) in Scorpius is overhead for southern observers in their "autumn" (March through June), and it is opposed seasonally to the real southern gem, Canopus (α Carinae), which is second only to Sirius in stellar brightness. Two other bright stars, Achernar (α Eridani) and Fomalhaut (α Pisces Austrini), are prominent overhead from about August through November.

Knowing what specific stars and their groupings to watch for is clearly significantly related to seasonality. In the interest of keeping time by the stars, some key concepts to be aware of include the following:

1. a star or star group's prominence overhead around midnight, which means these same bodies are likely to be rising at sunset and setting around sunrise;

2. the *heliacal rise* of a star, or its first rising or reappearance in the dawn sky just prior to sunrise after a period of nightly disappearance, after which the star will appear daily higher or rise earlier as the sun continues its annual eastward course through the stars (as opposed to its daily westward movement); and

3. *heliacal set*, which occurs at dusk and is the last sighting of a star prior to its conjunction with the sun that results in a period of disappearance or invisibility.

ZODIAC AND MILKY WAY

As mentioned above, the yearly path of the sun's apparent motion is called the ecliptic, and it is charted in the sky against the backdrop of what Western astronomy calls the constellations of the *zodiac*. There are twelve constellations in the zodiac, from Aries to Pisces, spaced along the band in 30° sections (that is about three hands'—or fists'—width). Our Western system of astrology is focused on this series of constellations and the positions of sun, moon, and planets relative to it, believing all of this to exert considerable influence on human affairs. Applying this system today, however, some 2,000 years since its inception, is problematic, due again to precession or the wobble of the Earth's axis of rotation. The annual origin point of our zodiacal system is the vernal equinox, that point where the sun on its ecliptic path simultaneously crosses the celestial equator, passing from south to north in its yearly apparent motion. (We observe the vernal or March equinox when the sun rises due east and sets due west on an ideal flat horizon.) The location of the vernal equinox also moves due to precession, shifting or precessing in a westward direction along the ecliptic. So, although the dates for horoscope readings assigned to Aries are March 21–April 20, these dates are based on the original location of the vernal equinox at the edge of the constellation Aries. However, the vernal equinox today, due to precession, is located near Aquarius at the edge of Pisces, Aries' western neighbor. Today the horoscopic dates for Aries are technically more accurate for Pisces while moving toward

Aquarius, and this will continue to change until the cycle of precession—the Earth's wobble—comes back around, the entire cycle taking almost 26,000 years.

Several issues relative to the zodiac are relevant, however, to students of ethnoastronomy. For one, this astrological use of astronomical observations in our own cultural history should enlighten us as to comparable uses by other societies. That celestial entities and events can and do influence the lives of humans is a common crosscultural notion, as can be seen in various examples throughout this book. In addition, the zodiacal constellations do map out the course of movement for sun, moon, and planets, so regardless of opinions about the efficacy of Western astrology, becoming familiar with these constellations is a practical way to locate the ecliptic and mark solar, lunar, and planetary progress along it. Additionally and not the least significant, several bright stars are present in what are often otherwise unremarkable and not always easily identifiable constellations. These bright stars, such as Aldebaran in Taurus, Castor and Pollux (α and β Geminorum) in Gemini, Regulus (α Leonis) in Leo, Spica (α Virginis) in Virgo and Antares (α Scorpii) in Scorpius, as more accessible identifiers of the ecliptic and help measure the pace of time flow along it. They also occasionally serve as noteworthy conjunctions with the moon and planets; such celestial proximities are always exciting to naked eye observers.

There are of course other regular phenomena in the night sky. One of the most interesting for many peoples is the **Milky Way**, our own **galaxy** as we see it, appearing as a luminous band or strands across the night sky. Not easy to see in skies tinted with artificial light or filmy with smog, for those with a clearer view of the heavens the extent of this band across the sky along with its unusual movement through the sky serve to interest and even awe star gazers. This seems especially true in the southern hemisphere, where a particularly noticeable section of it contrasts dramatically with α and β Centauri and the bright stars of the Southern Cross, gleaming like embedded gems in a celestial ornament. Here also is the Coalsack, which as indicated by its name, is a dark configuration—actually a **nebula** or mass of interstellar matter—appearing almost like a hole in the galaxy. In South America it is common for natives to perceive culturally pertinent shapes in especially the dark patches of the Milky Way, so-called "dark cloud" constellations (Urton, 1981), and as among the runa of Misminay, to perceive its orientation and movement with cosmological and calendrical significance (discussed in more detail below).

Also visible by southern observers are two fuzzy formations known as the Large and Small Magellanic Clouds. These too, like our Milky Way, are galaxies. They are positioned in such a way as to be in opposition to α and β Centauri and the Southern Cross, bracketing and therefore helping to locate the south celestial pole for southern observers.

CROSSCULTURAL SIGNIFICANCE OF STARS

Given the intent and scope of this work, it is not possible to include the many impressive stellar observations and systems of star-lore collected among non-Western peoples. The following is but a sampling to help stimulate interest and whet the appetite for more. When reading of such astronomical systems, however, please bear in mind that they are parts of much larger cultural systems of knowledge and practice that require time and sensitivity to grasp and appreciate more fully. Such systems were likely known by some members of the society better than others, and so learning the material has probably been typified by inconsistencies. In addition, there are strong indications that names for important stars or constellations were not always regularized or shared by all members of a society as a single cultural classificatory scheme, making stellar identifications more complicated and tenuous for the outsider.

As indicated in the descriptive passage introducing chapter 1 of this present book, Bororo men are in the habit, especially on clear and dry nights, of reclining on palm mats in the village plaza to view the myriad brightly colored stars in their firmament. And as the introductory passage to this chapter suggests, the stars are perceived, due to their brightness, color, and movement in ordered regularity, as "something beautiful," both aesthetically and as a pattern for appropriate relationships and responsibilities.[2]

The single most important stellar phenomenon to the Bororo are the Pleiades, coincidentally pluralized in Bororo as Akiri-doge (while *akiri* is "white down," the name actually refers to numerous small white or down-like flowers of the *akiri-i* [Bororo] or *angico* [Portuguese] plant, a tropical legume). This asterism is used to gauge the passage of time during the night, but also serves for seasonal timing of significant cultural activities. Their first heliacal rise at dawn in mid-June, after about a one-month disappearance from the sky, is traditionally the time for the definitive male coming-of-age ritual called Akiri-doge Ewure Kowudu or "The Burning of the Feet of the Pleiades." At the same time, their heliacal rise introduces the dry season and the long hunting/gathering treks that typify it. By the time the Pleiades are overhead at dawn, in mid-August, the Bororo predict strong winds, and as these die down about one month later, when the Pleiades are at an altitude of about 60° in the west at dawn, they say it is the time to burn their fields prior to planting. Planting time and the likely beginning of the rains coincide with the Pleiades at about 45° up from west at dawn in early October. The Pleiades are overhead at night during the rainy season, rising at dusk in late November, and as the rains are ending in late April and early May is when they have their heliacal set (Fabian, 1992:131–33). As impressive as this type of stellar calendar is, the Bororo do not refer to it exclusive of other temporal indicators. Solar position, lunar position and phase, and generally all environmental phenomena are considered when making plans for specific activities; but the traditional constant or emphasis here does seem to be the Pleiades observations.

What is remarkable about the Pleiades is how significant they seem to be in so many systems of native astronomy, especially as primary seasonal indicators. Even only brief research in publications on Native South Americans reveals numerous examples. For the Eastern Timbira the position of the Pleiades is used to predict the rainy season and so when to clear land for planting (Nimuendajú, 1946:233), while the Tapirapé of central Brazil use the Pleiades to forecast both rainy and dry seasons (Wagley, 1983 [1977]:50). The Tupinambá of the Brazilian coast likewise used this group to predict the coming of the rains (d'Abbeville, 1963 [1614]:317). Among the Barasana of the upper Amazon the Pleiades cycle is related not only to seasonality but to synchronizing with it the complex cycle of male initiation (Hugh-Jones, 1979:65–66). Among the runa of the central Peruvian Andes, the Pleiades are called "Storehouse," and are related to the cycle of maize cultivation (Urton, 1981:118–21).

Numerous other stars and constellations are observed by the Bororo (Fabian, 1992:chapter 7), including stars in Scorpius, Corvus, Orion, and Sagittarius (all prominent in June, a preferred month for laying out at night and observing stars due to climate and atmospheric conditions). Sirius has its own name (Tuwagowu, meaning unclear). α and β Centauri show up as Pari Bopona, "thigh of the rhea" (an ostrich-like bird) while the Southern Cross is either this bird's foot or track. What is really interesting here is that these stars are perceived together with black areas of the Milky Way, such as the Coalsack as the rhea's head, to configure the entire animal. Interestingly, the Eastern Timbira considerably to the north of the Bororo also see this rhea in the Milky Way (Nimuendajú, 1946:233). Other dark patches of the Milky Way are also identified by the Bororo, such as the areas near Sirius, which appear to the Bororo to resemble a large mortar and pestle. The Milky Way itself is called synonymously (I)Kuieje-doge Erugudu ("the ash—or light/luster—of the stars"), Ipare Erugudu ("the ash—or light/luster—of the youths"), or Ipare Eguru ("the tears of the youths"), which may all be references in some way to the origin of the stars myth that begins this chapter. What is quite clear, even under current conditions of acculturation, is that the Bororo have an active and practiced familiarity with much that goes on in the sky, using stars for time reckoning and activity planning, as references to mythic texts and messages, and generally as patterns full of cultural relevance.

Gary Urton (1981) presents rich details of runa stellar lore from Misminay in the Andes. As related above, the Pleiades are important here as Collca or Storehouse: ". . . the Pleiades are used primarily to help determine when planting should commence and as a preplanting indication of how good the coming year's crop will be" (Urton, 1981:118). Celestial crosses and/or bridges (conceptually related in pre-conquest Quechua societies in the term *chaca(na)* as "bridge" or "crossbeam" [129–32]) also have prominence in Andean stellar lore. Included in this category are the Southern Cross itself and Orion's Belt. These apparently interrelated constellations have heavy symbolic and cosmological significance for Quechua speakers, and in a complex system of spatial and temporal alignments and oppositions help organize space and time in a way that emphasizes a state of sociocultural equilibrium (Urton, 1981:ch. 7). Perhaps the most intriguing set of constellations among the Quechua speakers, however, is their system of Yana Phuyu or "dark cloud" figures perceived within the Milky Way (Urton, 1981:ch. 9). All of these figures are animals including a llama (or two), a toad, a serpent, two tinamous, and a fox, which stretch across major portions of the Milky Way and are associated with the terrestrial cycles of these creatures. However, besides this more mundane correlation, these figures "serve as the focus for a number of important classificatory and symbolic principles in the astronomy and cosmology of Misminay" including color oppositions and associations, concepts of fertility, and spatial and temporal orientation (189–90). It is critical to point out, however, that as with the Bororo, full meaning of the people of Misminay's stellar observations derive from their coordination with numerous other cultural and environmental factors.

In the tropics north of the equator, the classic Maya are well known for their interest in and use of astronomy, including building alignments, site directionality, tables of day counts relevant to Venus, and various other relevant cultural practices (see, for example, Aveni, 1980 and 1989a). Contemporary Maya of Momostenango in the Guatemalan highlands continue some of this tradition, according to Barbara Tedlock (1992). They label "all of the celestial bodies—sun, moon, planets, comets, meteors, stars, asterisms, constellations, and the Milky Way" *ch'umilal caj*, "starry sky" (179). These phenomena are watched and discussed with particular interest by initiated daykeepers who serve as "calendar diviners, dream interpreters, and curers" (47), in a complex system of synchronizing natural, agricultural, ritual, and personal cycles in a very dense cosmology. Numerous individual stars and constellations are known, and among the more calendrically significant are the Pleiades and Regulus, as well as stars in Orion, Gemini, and the Big Dipper. The theme of fire seems common in several identifications such as Spica as pix, "spark"; Rigel as *nima k'ak'*, "big fire"; and Orion's Belt as *je oxib chi k'ak' ajaw*, "tail of the three fire lords." While no dark cloud constellations are mentioned, the Milky Way has two names for two perceived segments, the "undivided segment" called *saki be* or "white road" and the segment with a "dark cleft" known as *xibalba be* or "underworld road" (B. Tedlock, 1992:ch. 8).

North of the Maya in the U.S. Southwest, the Navajo occupy a sprawling reservation in the Four Corners area. This space represents a definitive advantage in the efforts of traditionalists to maintain indigenous identity and practices. In her sensitive treatment of Navajo sandpainting, Trudy Griffin-Pierce (1992) relates that Navajo constellations, like landscape features, link "the mythic past with the physical present" by evoking the memory of traditional narratives and their "underlying moral component" (142). As "cultural texts" with their embedded meanings, certain prominent constellations are replicated in another type of cultural text, sacred and living sandpaintings used in healing ceremonies, while "stargazing" is one of the active means of divination that can "determine the etiology of illness, the source of misfortune, or the location of missing objects" (143). For sandpaintings, the eight major constellations named are the Big Dipper, Cassiopeia, the Pleiades, Orion, Corvus, two differentiated sections of Scorpius, and the Milky Way (78). The stars in general were created to provide light in the absence of the moon, and "to provide seasonal and nightly markers for agricultural, hunting, and ceremonial activities" (83). For example, Gah heet'e'ii, "rabbit tracks" or the tail of Scorpius, helps determine when to hunt, and the Big Dipper and Cassiopeia in opposition across from each other but centered around Polaris, are both called Náhookos, "The Male and Female One Who Revolve," and represent a number of marriage, relationship, and residence laws (87). The Pleiades, Dilyéhé, may be used to represent all the constellations in some depictions, and are watched as a seasonal indicator and for telling nightly time, and are perceived as "epitomizing the Navajo emphasis on order and balance" (158). While astronomical knowledge itself may be of "a highly specialized nature" among the Navajo (172), nevertheless it seems obvious that in one way or another it profoundly affects their lives.

Further north, another indigenous society with a pronounced interest in stellar observations is the traditionally semi-nomadic Skidi band of Pawnee of the Prairie/Plains area. According to Von Del Chamberlain (1982), the Skidi observed a wide range of astronomical phenomena in a well-developed system. Skidi astronomical observations served as the basis for a Pawnee calendar of major agricultural and other activities, the orientation and form/structure of their Earth lodges, their origin myth and other important folkloristic texts, and as patterns for appropriate cultural behavior. First, the Skidi consider their very origin to be celestial: the original human (a female) was born from the cosmic mating of White Star and Morning Star (possibly actually planets; see chapter 5), while her counterpart, the first male, came as the offspring of Sun and Moon (223–24). Building on this cosmic theme, the Skidi Earth lodge was "to be like the heavens," with a rounded shape; an east-facing doorway in the direction of thinking, planning, and the origin of heat and light; and a smoke-hole overhead in the direction of origin and wisdom and from which astronomical observations were made (227). As a model for leadership, the Skidi look to the "Star-that-does-not-move," or Polaris, who stands as a "symbol of stability, leadership, and guardianship" and "to some extent [is] representative of *Tirawahat*, the creator god" (225), while the circular corona borealis is their pattern for a council of chiefs. As expected, the Pleiades are not ignored: as the "Seven Stars," they serve as a model of unity. The Milky Way is considered the path for departed spirits (230–31). Of course, as with the previously described systems, this short sampling of Skidi astronomy falls far short of adequately representing the richness, beauty, and complexity of their native system.

On their reservation in the northern plains, modern-day Crow Indians keep alive much of their traditional stellar knowledge and interest. Timothy McCleary (1997) reports that stars, *ihké*, are considered spherical in shape, and "are perceived as powerful beings who can provide assistance to humans" (15). They are watched regularly in the early part of the night following sunset and also before sunrise, and although the Crow were nomadic food foragers and buffalo hunters rather than farmers, they still observed the stars as a gauge for their seasonal activities, with Sirius, Bright Star, being the most utilized in this respect (20–21). The circumpolar Seven Stars/Seven Brothers/Seven Buffalo Bulls or Big Dipper have various meanings, associations, and applications. They are important for telling night time and also help to locate "the star that does not move around," Polaris, used for basic directional orientation (24–26), but also symbolize "brotherly love" and are "a model of how people should ideally work together" (80). They are also associated with the sweatlodge and its meaning and the performance of its sacred sweat ceremony, as are the Pleiades, known as The Gathering of Stars (73–79). The Milky Way takes its name, Where They Take Women, from a story about wife abduction and rescue, and its position "is seen as an indicator of clear or stormy weather" (106). The stars helped the Crow settle in their homeland, and in general serve their practical, spiritual, and moral needs. As McCleary attests, "A Crow cannot take a sweat, nurture a child, care properly for a relative, engage in ritual, create art, discuss philosophy, or tell cosmic time without some knowledge of the stars" (109).

Among far northern peoples, Subarctic tribes such as the Eastern Cree identify the Big Dipper as Fisher (a member of the weasel family) Stars and Polaris as Great Star or Guide of the People, while the Milky Way is Ghost Road, and Orion's Belt is seen as Three Chiefs (Miller, 1997:chapter 4). The Yukon-centered Kutchin on the Arctic Circle are reported as telling time in the winter by use of the Big Dipper (Osgood,

1936:102). East of the Kutchin, the Central Eskimo were found by Boas to "distinguish a number of constellations," the most important of which are Tuktuqdjung, "caribou," in Ursa Major (perhaps the Big Dipper?), Saki-etaun, Pleiades, and two with problematic names configured in Orion, one of which relates to folklore about three men hunting a bear (1888:636–43). Far to the west, Bering Strait Inuit see the Pleiades as a litter of fox cubs, identify Sirius as Moon Dog and use it to predict high winds when in proximity to the moon, and tell of the culture hero Raven's walk on snowshoes en route to creating humans as the Milky Way (Miller, 1997:88).

A rich source of star and astronomical information from the Arctic is found in John MacDonald's (1998) research and work among the Inuit of Igloolik. He includes detailed discussions of sixteen prominent stars and constellations, including the Pleiades and Sirius, Polaris and the Big Dipper, Orion and Cassiopeia (chapter 3). Among the Inuit, as reported by MacDonald, stars may be "mythic transformations of earthly humans and animals," and often have "practical uses" such as in calculating seasonal and diurnal time, especially around the winter solstice; for navigation; in weather prediction; and as a source for shamanic power (38–40).

The above serves as a representative sampling of some of the range, depth, complexity, and beauty of stellar lore and its application among Native American peoples. The more systematic studies clearly present native astronomies as intimately interrelated with virtually all facets of culture. As such, they are vulnerable to disuse and loss under even moderate conditions of assimilation and acculturation, since in such conditions their specific cultural correlations and underpinnings generally are stripped away. It is common in native systems to encounter either multiple names for the same star or constellation, or different bodies for which the same name may be applied, due at times to underlying structural and cosmological relations between these stars, as well as the individualization and specialization of this corpus of knowledge. Although it may seem that these ethnoastronomical systems are crude in contrast to the formal grid of 88 constellations with which modern Western astronomy systematically organizes the nocturnal sky, native sophistication in observation, knowledge of cycles, and multi-dimensionality of their understanding and use must be appreciated. This is especially important to keep in mind, since, in spite of the richness of much native starlore, our record and understanding of indigenous astronomical systems is most often fragmentary.

EXERCISES: STELLAR OBSERVATIONS

Exercise 4.1   Finding polar constellations
As part of the exercises in chapter 1 you should already have located either Polaris or the region of the south celestial pole. Since the

surrounding stars are often used as an aid to do this, this exercise may
be somewhat redundant. Nevertheless, after locating the celestial pole
of your hemisphere, draw and identify the major stars nearest to it. For
this and all observations, be sure to record the date and time of your
observation, any pertinent horizon features and their altitude, and the
altitude and azimuth of your identified objects.

Exercise 4.2   Stars on the celestial equator

The most famous and easily identifiable stars on the celestial
equator are Orion's Belt, generally a late fall to winter sky feature in
the north (reverse the seasonality south of the equator). Altair (α Aquilae) and the constellation Aquila are nearly opposite Orion on the far
side of the celestial equator. Remember that the celestial equator is 90°
from your celestial pole. This means that if Polaris is up 40°, estimate
the zenith directly overhead, then move 40° past it (southward) along
the meridian to approximate the point where the equator crosses it.
Identify and record your observation of the stars in this area. Knowing
that the celestial equator intersects the idealized flat horizon at the
east and west cardinal points, locate these (as close as your local viewing conditions allow) and identify and record your observation of the
pertinent stars. Once you make recordings of the point of meridian
intersection and eastern and western extremes of the celestial equator,
try to make a complete recording of the major visible stars along its
entire length.

Exercise 4.3   Identifying the ecliptic

The sun's location on the ecliptic extends to 23½° north of the
celestial equator in the daytime in June, resulting in the solstice
extreme of the sun. But this means that the corresponding part of the
ecliptic on summer nights is south of the celestial equator (reverse
these directions for winter). Since you know that the ecliptic runs
through the constellations of the zodiac, try to locate the visible portion
of the ecliptic. Where does it cross the meridian? Where does it intersect with your horizon? Can you identify the constellations along its
entire visible length? Try this exercise twice, half a year apart, for a
more complete picture of the ecliptic position and diversity.

Exercise 4.4   Nightly stellar motion

As discussed in chapter 2, many Native North Americans refer to
clockwise motion as "sunwise," since on a daily basis the sun in the temperate latitudes can be seen rising in the east, coursing up into the
southern portion of the sky, then setting in the west, movement that is
left-to-right. Once it is dark enough to see a number of stars, make and
record an initial observation of stars either on the eastern horizon or
along the meridian opposite your celestial pole. Then make a separate
observation of stars that are nearest your celestial pole at the meridian.

About an hour later, make a second set of observations of the same stars you recorded in your previous observations. How far have they gone? In what direction?

Exercise 4.5   Stars as a nighttime clock

Many peoples discussed in this chapter use specific constellations to mark the passing of night time. Can you begin to do the same? Select either a rising star/constellation after sunset or any prominent star group with which you feel familiar and make and record your initial observation. Follow this up in an hour, and note how far it has gone. Can you predict where it will be in another hour? Where will a star that is on the eastern horizon at sunset be at midnight? At sunrise?

Exercise 4.6   Stars and seasonal time

If time allows, make and record an initial observation of the night sky after sunset or at midnight, and follow up this observation one month later, and again a month after that. In your follow-up observation(s), identify and record your initial reference star/constellation and its new location as well as a comparison star/constellation now located where your reference body was at your initial observation.

Exercise 4.7   Heliacal rise and set

You may need help from an almanac or other source in timing these observations, especially observing the heliacal rise, which will be more noteworthy to you if you can actually precede the heliacal rise by a previous observation a night or two ahead of the predicted rise.

For the heliacal rise, look in the east just before the disappearance of stars at dawn and record this, then follow this up with another observation or two on subsequent mornings. Did some new star appear? Identify and record.

For the heliacal set, observe and record the western horizon as soon as stars become visible after sunset. Follow up on succeeding nights until you no longer "see" something that was there during your initial observation.

Endnotes

[1] For more detailed published versions see Colbacchini and Albisetti, 1942:218–19; Albisetti and Venturelli (1964):#22; Wilbert and Simoneau (1983):#18 and #19, pp. 47–51; and Fabian (1992, pp. 126–28.)

[2] Working from published documents of earlier researchers and my own fieldwork, I have endeavored to present as complete (if not exhaustive) and clear a picture of Bororo astronomy and stellar observations as possible in my work *Space-Time of the Bororo of Brazil*, 1992. See especially chapter 7.

Chapter Five

The Planets

Darkness came shortly after the sunset, and the blue of the tropical night sky was rich and deep, washed clean by the wet days of *butaokau* or "rainy season." It was mid-February, and we were fortunate to have such a clear evening, with the night's first stars beginning to sparkle overhead.

I stood outside of the shaggy silhouette of our palm-draped house, in the back patio area scraped clean of grass and brush. An elder of the Bokodori Exerae clan was with me, his white hair tinted with the sunset's glorious palette. We looked westward, to *meributu*, over the scattered shrubs and trees and rolling hills of the savanna, appreciating the natural beauty.

There to the west was a young and waxing crescent moon and near it, in the afterglow of the setting sun, Venus as Evening Star brightened to the night's deepening dark.

Motioning toward the brilliant planet with my chin, I remarked on its beauty in Portuguese.

"Uu, yes," the elder replied, "Orowaribo Kajijewu is bright tonight."

"Orowaribo Kajijewu? What does that mean?"

"Umm . . ." he muttered, taking awhile to render the concept in his second language. "'It is over the large water,' that's what we say."

I noted this and clarified with him that the "large water" referred to the Paraguay River, many kilometers distant and an apparent dividing line in early historical accounts between eastern and western groups of Bororo. Then I inquired further on the nature of Orowaribo Kajijewu.

"Orowaribo Kajijewu is only in the west," replied the elder. "In the east we say Jekurireu, we call it 'the large face.'"

THE FIVE VISIBLE "WANDERERS"

In the previous chapter, important qualities of the stars were described that facilitate their use for time reckoning and other cultural purposes. These include their grouping in patterns or constellations that are arranged in a fixed and continuous sequence, moving in ordered regularity with respect to the annual cycle. Planets, although appearing star-like especially to the casual or infrequent sky observer, actually conform to none of these stellar characteristics.

Our English word "planet" comes from the Greek *planes*, or "wanderer," an apt concept. In contrast to the fixed positions of stars relative to each other and their orderly movement with respect to a yearly cycle, when observed carefully or regularly the planets appear to "wander" with respect to the patterns and positions of the more stable stars, and do so in periodicities not neatly commensurate with our year. The stars, being objects far distant from our solar system, appear to maintain their positions relative to each other and their regular motion as we on Earth revolve around the sun over the course of a year; you may have noticed a similar phenomenon from inside a moving vehicle while observing far distant features of the terrain. But the planets are much closer and share our solar system with us, and so just as from the same moving vehicle you would see objects closer to you moving faster than those farther away, so too as we move on Earth we observe the closer planets to move relative to the more distant stars. But this explanation only accounts for some of their apparent motion, for the planets, as part of our solar system, also revolve around the sun, moving in their own cycles even as we on Earth move in ours.

Of the several planets present in our solar system, five are visible to the naked eye. Moving outward from the sun these are Mercury and Venus, known as *inferior* or *inner planets* in their location between Earth and sun, and Mars, Jupiter, and Saturn, known as *superior* or *outer planets* in their orbits beyond that of Earth's. These designations are significant, since as Earth-based observers we see different planetary motions for these two categories. For both categories, naked eye astronomers likely would be most interested in their synodic periods of movement, that is, their positioning relative to the sun from our perspective as Earth-based observers (rather than in the "true" cycle of their revolution or orbit around the sun).

VENUS AND MERCURY: ATTACHED TO THE SUN

As inferior planets, Mercury and Venus have orbits smaller than Earth's, and our observation of them is affected by their passage between

Earth and the sun, as well as by their passage on the far side of the sun: these conjunctions with the sun result in their temporary disappearance from view. For inferior planets, two conjunctions or periods of disappearance occur in a complete synodic cycle.

Venus is the brightest "star" or star-like light in the sky, with some variation in its brightness—as is true for all planets—due to its position relative to Earth and the sun. Planets "glow" by reflecting sunlight, as opposed to stars, which are suns shining in their own right; recalling the moon's phases due to its changing position relative to Earth and sun might help you imagine why some changes occur in planetary brightness. From our position outside of the orbits of the two inferior planets, they appear to us to never move very far away from the sun. Since they are primarily visible in the east around sunrise and in the west near sunset, the inferior planets, especially Venus, are commonly seen as Morning or Evening Star (see figure 4).

What does the movement of Venus and Mercury actually look like to us? Imagine that Venus and the sun are in conjunction and that therefore Venus has disappeared from view. Then one dawn Venus reappears over the eastern horizon just before sunrise. By observing Venus day after day, we would see it appear further away (and earlier in the predawn darkness) from the sun on successive mornings. At its farthest separation from the sun about 130 days later, Venus is more than 45° distant, rising into the sky about three hours ahead of the sun (Aveni, 1980:85). By continuing to observe daily we would next see Venus returning closer to the sun, until it disappears once more in conjunction with the sun. We would now need to shift our observations to the evening, when Venus eventually will reappear just after and near sunset, and then will increase its distance and time away from the sun on successive nights until its furthest separation. After shining brightly in the west in the early night sky, Venus will then return again to conjunction with the sun. Venus's appearances as Morning Star and Evening Star are each 263 days long, while its two disappearances differ markedly: it takes about 8 days for its passage in front of the sun en route to becoming the Morning Star, and more or less 50 days to transit behind the sun before returning as Evening Star. The entire Venus synodic period totals 584 days (Aveni, 1980:89).

Mercury's movement is similar, but more challenging to see as it is dimmer than Venus and stays even closer to the sun, where observations of it are more vulnerable to atmospheric effects and horizon obstructions. For those able to observe Mercury regularly, its periodicity is somewhat more dramatic than that of Venus: visible periods at dawn and dusk are only about 38 days each, with disappearances averaging 5 and 35 days, respectively, and a total synodic period of only 116 days (Aveni, 1980:89).

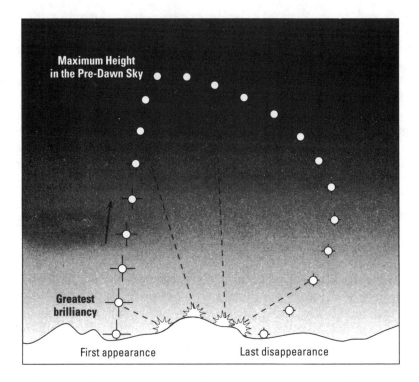

Figure 4. Venus as morning star. Standing in the same spot and following the motion of Venus from night to night at the same time of night, this is an example of what you would see. Symbols spaced at two-week intervals show where Venus would just disappear toward dawn in the east over several months. As Venus makes a sweeping arc across the sky from first appearance at horizon, through maximum altitude, to last disappearance below the horizon, the sun, connected to it by a dashed line, creeps along the horizon, southward. The sizes of the spikes on the Venus symbol denote relative brightness. This looped track is one of five distinct shapes the course of Venus can take in the morning or evening sky.

MARS, JUPITER, AND SATURN

For Earth-based observers, these superior planets manifest very different patterns of movement from the two inferior planets just described. Our vantage point inside of their orbits results in three important and different characteristics from our observations of the inner planets. First, Mars, Jupiter, and Saturn are not limited to close proximity with the sun, and we can therefore see them across the full extent of the night sky, limited of course within the plane of the ecliptic or our zodiacal constellations. Second, we will see them in conjunction with the sun only once in their synodic cycles, as they pass behind the solar orb. And third, our ability to "catch up" to and go by them on our inner orbit results in a curious motion known as ***retrograde motion***, when a superior planet will actually appear to move *backward* against a backdrop of stars.

All three planets normally will appear to move in an eastward direction through the constellations on successive nights. During retrograde, which occurs when the planet is farthest from conjunction with the sun or in ***opposition***, the planet's eastward progress will slow, stop, and then appear to reverse itself in a westward movement before slowing, stopping, and then resuming its original direction. Of course, careful and consistent observation over time is necessary to observe this phenomenon. The synodic periods for Mars, Jupiter, and Saturn average, respectively, 780, 399, and 378 days.

CROSSCULTURAL OBSERVATIONS OF THE PLANETS

Do native peoples make consistent enough astronomical observations to recognize the planets as phenomena distinct from the stars? Are their cycles noted? Are the morning and evening appearances of Mercury and Venus recognized as being of the same celestial body? Is retrograde observed, and if so, how is it explained? These and other questions indicate some of the challenges in researching planetary observations in non-Western astronomical systems.

Detailed published information on planetary observations in indigenous societies is rare. We must wonder if this is due to lack of interest or knowledge on the natives' part or possibly on the part of ethnographers. An ethnographer would be most receptive to and likely would report more accurately issues of planetary and other astronomical lore with some prior understanding of astronomy, but training in astronomy is hardly required background for ethnographic fieldworkers. Also, difficulties arise with observations of the planets, since their movements and periodicities are not well synchronized with the solar year and are somewhat irregular with respect to where and when one might expect to find them (and so accurately identify them in the field). What extent of consistent astronomical observations allows for the fullest comprehension and reporting of planetary phenomena? Such observations would be particularly challenging during shorter periods of field study. Some of these difficulties may be surmounted by accessing appropriate planetary references while in the field; unfortunately, these are not likely to be part of the average ethnographer's tool kit.

By virtue of their very irregularity with respect to the year and stars, however, I would argue that planets can be significant components of observational systems, especially for prognostications or as omens. I've argued elsewhere (Fabian, 1992:144–45) that it is because of their relative discontinuity with respect to other more regular or continuous cycles that phenomena such as the planets (as well as the moon and its phases) have predictive value in systems of time reckoning. Evidence for this exists in our Western astrology and the significance accompanying the location of the planets (as well as the sun and moon) in the different zodiacal houses. Also, among the ancient Maya, Venus, as an anthropomorphized deity, seemed to be watched, at least in its Morning Star role, as a harbinger of (mostly) ill fortune (Aveni, 1980:26).

As indicated in the descriptive passage introducing this chapter, some Bororo recognize Venus as both Morning and Evening Star, though separate names are used for the planet in each position. However, there were five different names applied to Venus during the course of my fieldwork among the Bororo, including a reference to its spatial position (while in the west), a temporal component (accompanying the dawn), and its brightness. Mars was named the (red) eye of a bird whose call is heard as a good hunting omen, and Jupiter was given one of three designations used to indicate a morning star, all such designations possibly being linked to a traditional system of wake-up calls rousing the village to the day's activity (Fabian, 1992, especially 141–45).

Also in South America, the runa of Misminay observe several phenomena that are planets, including a "dawn of the Earth/time star" as Venus, a "dawn star" as an outer planet, a "zenith star" as an outer planet, and an "evening star" as Venus or an outer planet (Urton, 1981:166–67). Definitive identification is problematic, and it seems that a first magnitude star (that is, among the brightest of stars) might substitute for all but the "dawn star" for the runa (166–67). Further south, in Tierra del Fuego, the Ona are reported to observe the planet Mars as a red star sent by the sun and moon to Earth, where as a giant he killed the existing humans and then fashioned two mounds from which rose the first Ona man and woman (Cooper, 1917:163).

In the northern Tropics, contemporary Quiché Maya recognize at least some planets as a group, which they call "red stars" and which they associate particularly with morning and evening star identities. For these Maya the planet manifesting as Morning Star is named "sun carrier," while the evening star is known as "of the night" (B. Tedlock, 1992:180). As data for the Bororo, runa of Misminay, and the Maya indicate, it seems common for native groups to apply general morning and evening star designations to whatever planet is best identified in that role at any given time. Following data on these same peoples, it appears that bright stars also may be substituted for planets if no planets currently occupy a significant structural position (e.g., as Morning or Evening Star).

The Skidi Pawnee actually performed one of the most sensational practices associated with the observation of planets: the occasional sacrifice of human life (usually a maiden) to the Great Star or Morning Star. In his analysis of this complex event, Chamberlain (1982) concludes that Mars is the most likely candidate as the "star" in question, although Venus and Jupiter are not ruled out; he sees "pragmatic needs" of the Skidi as the main impetus behind the occasional rite, with astronomical observation secondary (89). Venus is identified as Evening or White Star, a sky god, beautiful woman, and mother of the first human being perceived as "the female element, the first mother, the agricultural deity . . . [who] directed acts of creation, communication with life on Earth, and renewed the flow of life each spring" (52–55). Jupiter or Mercury may have been brother to the Morning Star and called Second Morning Star, and Saturn may have been a "Star of Disease" against which ritual acts, such as the burning of sweetgrass, were thought to provide some protection (91). As with the other data on planets described above, identification problems stem from planetary irregularities in appearance and position.

The irregularity of planets in contrast with the other stars is highlighted by one of the Crow terms for Venus: "Crazy Star." Recognizing Venus in both its morning and evening roles, one Crow elder described how, because of its changing color, its sparkling and its flashing, and its disappearances and reappearances but in different places, it was considered unpredictable and "crazy" and was therefore not used to fix times/seasons, nor was it sought for religious power. Mars is also known as a Morning Star and for its red color and is personified as a young woman in Crow folklore (McCleary, 1997:43–47).

Among the Arctic Inuit, weather conditions and prolonged periods of summer light make the consistent observation of planets that is necessary for an accurate grasp of their cycles difficult at best. MacDonald (1998) reports that Venus, Jupiter, Mars, and Saturn as a group are called Ulluriaqjuat or "Great Stars." The singular "Great Star" is especially applied to Venus, in both its morning and evening appearances (92). Some indigenous use of especially Venus may have been made as a time indicator, but changing cultural practices, modern Christian influences, and problematic identifications in ethnohistorical documents all limit our precise understanding of celestial entities among the Inuit.

It is very likely that without formal training in astronomy and an up-to-date knowledge of the location of all visible planets during the period of fieldwork, an ethnographer could easily misidentify planets. Consistent observations are needed to distinguish clearly planets from stars and especially to have some sense of their synodical periodicities. That various native peoples with different economic and sociopolitical structures are known to possess some such knowledge should alert us to more interest in this topic and greater receptivity to indigenous observational systems.

EXERCISES: INFERIOR/INNER AND SUPERIOR/ OUTER PLANET OBSERVATIONS

Exercise 5.1   Inferior or inner planets
Using information available to you in an almanac, astronomy magazines, Web sites, or any source that covers planetary positions, determine where Mercury and Venus may be (as Evening or Morning Stars) during the period of your active observations (one or both may be in conjunction with the sun and so temporarily invisible). With star chart in hand, make your own identification of one or both, noting and drawing the neighboring stars, proximity of horizon, and altitude and azimuth. Carefully note the time. Make at least one more such observation on a later date to determine any change in the planet's position. Is the planet currently moving away from or closer to the sun?

Exercise 5.2   Relationship to sunrise, sunset
Once you are able to recognize these planets, record the time of sunset (last gleam) or sunrise (first gleam), whichever is pertinent. Make at least one observation to determine how much time transpires between sunset and the first visibility of the evening star planet(s), or the time between the disappearance at dawn of the morning star planet(s) and sunrise. Make at least one follow-up observation to determine if the time is increasing or decreasing, then compare this with your observations in exercise 5.1.

Exercise 5.3   Superior or outer planets
Again using information available to you, determine where Mars, Jupiter, and/or Saturn may be during the period of your active observations (one or all may be in conjunction with the sun and so temporarily invisible). With star chart in hand, make your own identification of one or any, noting and drawing the neighboring stars (remember that all planets course along the ecliptic, which is marked by our zodiacal constellations), proximity of horizon, and altitude and azimuth. Carefully note the time. Make at least one more such observation on a later date to determine any change in each planet's position. Based on your observations, are any of these planets currently in a state of retrograde?

Chapter Six

Other Celestial Phenomena

Climbing vertically in the blue midmorning sky, the sun at this stage of the dry season—Jorukau as the Bororo call it, or "Season of Fire"—was not yet obscured by the smoke of the many fires that burn at this time of year. Although strong, the heat was not oppressive, and few flying and biting pests were active. All in all this made for an enjoyable outing as I accompanied several men and boys on a fishing expedition.

In mostly single file we traversed the *boku* (Bororo) or *cerrado* (Portuguese), the mixed vegetation of grasses, shrubs, and trees of the tropical savanna. Intermittently we would stop to swim and fish in the cool, dark streams of the region. The fishing was done by hand-held nets while wading in the murky waters (chancing an accidental step on a stingray submerged in the sandy bottoms), or with lines or bow and arrow, all of which the men manipulated with considerable skill.

As meri (sun) climbed higher, we picked our way across bare rock shelves on the sides of a trickling creek that would surely dry up in the rainless weeks ahead. Then the men stopped and exclaimed excitedly, encouraging the boys among us forward. There ahead of us, basking in the sun on a heated slab of stone, was a young anaconda, perhaps six to eight feet in length. Disturbed from its sun bath, the anaconda began to move off, but was prevented from going far by the men who grabbed it by the tail and pulled it back into the open, at the same time urging the youths to come forward and touch it. By touching this handsome and largest of South American serpents, the youths would grow and strengthen and be beautiful as adults.

Jure, the Bororo word for anaconda, is also their term for rainbow. Anacondas frequent water, an association also made with the rainbow, and both are related to fertility and the natural fecundity and life of a bounteous nature. Jure is also a serpentine dance for maturing youths and adults that is associated by myth with the maturation of a young, male Bororo culture hero. After an incestuous act with his mother, this youth overcomes serious obstacles to bring ritually significant rattles—the "noise of culture"—back to his people. That the fat of the anaconda is a preferred medium for mixing with red dye to make body paint used to adorn the body in ritual contexts furthers the symbolic relationship between snake, ritual, dance, and rainbow. To the Bororo, all are fundamental expressions of beauty, fecundity, and vitality.

The sun, moon, and stars are obvious foci of attention for all native peoples, even though the extent to or way in which they are observed and utilized may vary greatly from culture to culture. As either a special category of "stars," or a punctuating presence in the more regular coursing of nightly phenomena, the planets also demand attention by all who observe the stars regularly. These phenomena are therefore properly the main focus of interest for ethnoastronomers, who must be ever-sensitive to learning the culturally specific and relative ideas and practices relevant to these awesome celestial entities. But beyond these standard features of astronomical interest, other elements are likely to be present in any specific society's astronomical repertoire. Some of these additional phenomena as described by our own Western perspective that may have specific cultural importance include comets, shooting stars or meteors, solar and lunar halos, rainbows, the aurora borealis, and even the sky itself.

THE VISIBLE SKY

The sky: overarching, painted brightly blue, patched with fluffy white or solidly gray, sunrise and sunset in dazzling pastels, star-studded or moonlit; but what is it? Our Western cosmology posits the sky as our window on an infinite universe, a window colored by our atmosphere and its associated characteristics and processes. But what is the sky for other peoples? How have they understood is presence?

For some peoples the sky has solidity, or is perceived to have layers. Early fieldworkers among the Bororo report a cosmology explaining the sky in three layers: white the lowest, red the middle, and blue the highest, in which certain spirit beings dwell or through which they move (see Colbacchini and Albisetti, 1942; Albisetti and Venturelli, 1962 under *baru* references; and Fabian, 1992:197–98). Certainly some Bororo myths, such as that of the origin of stars summarized at the beginning of chapter 4, indicate that the sky is a firmament of substance, apparently much like the ground, on which large trees, such as the South American sucupira, may grow.

Elsewhere in South America, the layering is not so apparent. As reported earlier in chapter 4, in Misminay in the Peruvian Andes to the west of the Bororo, the runa see the Milky Way as a celestial river, while various animals and other features occupy dark cloud and star-to-star constellations (Urton, 1981). That these celestial features are more than immaterial images or reflections of terrestrial phenomena is apparent in much of Gary Urton's discussion of the runa information. The following statement emphasizes this: "The water within the celestial River has a terrestrial origin, so it is not surprising to find that the animals of the Milky Way also originate from the earth. According to one informant in Misminay, the yana phuyu ('dark clouds') are actual pieces of earth taken up into the sky by the Milky Way" (174). Clearly, this implies some substance to the sky itself. North of the Bororo within 5° of the equator, the Eastern Timbira believe that vultures and falcons dwell in the sky, where they have human form and run log races and celebrate festivals (Nimuendajú, 1946:234).

In the tropics north of the equator we return to a layered cosmos. The Maya of Mesoamerica perceive multiple layers to occupy the sky in which reside the "sun, moon, stars, planets, and (since the Spanish invasion) Christian deities and saints" (B. Tedlock, 1992:173). And for the Navajo in the Southwest, "The celestial realm consists of two layers: the Sky World, in which are located the Sun, Moon, and Stars, and the Land-Beyond-the-Sky, inhabited by supremely powerful storm elements" (Griffin-Pierce, 1992:141).

As mentioned earlier in chapter 2, the Cherokee of the North American Southeast traditionally believe the sky to be an arch or vault of solid rock along the inside of which the sun climbs as a human figure during the day, returning at night on the upper side of the rock vault. The sun (and moon? other celestial entities?) is able to pass from one side of the sky vault to the other as the rock swings up and down, at sunset and sunrise (Mooney, 1982 [1900]:256). Further north, in the Plains, the Crow people "describe the heavens as a plane that over-arcs the earth . . . or another solid world that exists above the earth" where the sun, moon, and stars that dwell there (with the clouds and the birds) live "much like humans" (McCleary, 1997:15). This theme is continued into the Arctic, where the Inuit of Quebec "conceived [the sky] as a rigid dome resting on a flat earth with abrupt edges like those of the sea" (D'Anglure, 1984:495), and the Nunivak Eskimo thought of the sky as "a series of sky-worlds, one above the other" (Lantis, 1984:220). In general the Inuit perceive the sky as "a solid, arching canopy," which is the abode of souls and the personification of Sun and Moon (MacDonald, 1998:31). Stars are often described by these Arctic dwellers as holes in the sky, providing access to other celestial spaces above (MacDonald, 1998:32–33).

But whether solid and layered or not, the sky is not simply another mundane space. Often the abode of spirits and deities or the locus of potent spiritual forces, the sky for many peoples is a repository of power: fecund, regenerative, and spiritual power. This power is shared with the residents of the Earth via the sun's light, the rain, and other natural forces, as well as through spiritual connections. These spiritual connections may also have physical manifestations, such as for the Ojibwa as reported by Thor Conway. Making use of a "conjuror's lodge" of covered poles open at the top, a certain category of Ojibwa shamans known as "soul men" would seek to access directly the power of the spirit world in its celestial location through a hole in the sky associated with the Pleiades, the only opening between the star and spirit world and Earth. Conway (1992) writes that this hole is "an opening that breathes the transmission of spiritual power back and forth from this world to the star world. Whenever a shaman needs to recharge his or her power, soul-flight travel is used to reach this Hole in the Sky and cross the barrier to the spirit realm" (253).

The spiritual connection with the sky is reiterated on the Arctic Circle by the Central Eskimo as reported by Franz Boas from his field-work there in the 1880s. In general Boas (1888) describes the sky as an abode of powerful supernatural beings, usually anthropomorphized, who are "owners" of the stars, constellations, and meteorological pro-cesses. In times of cultural crisis an Eskimo shaman might find it nec-essary to take a spirit trip to the moon or other locale to propitiate hos-tile and influential spirits (594–97).

The sky may be conceptualized as an entire entity with gender attributes, such as "Father Sky" among the Mescalero Apache, which exists in complementary opposition to—and union with—"Mother Earth" (Farrer, 1991:113). This terminology is shared by their Athapas-kan-speaking relatives, the Navajo. The use of kinship terms for what we might consider natural features stresses the perceived personal relationship between humans and the nonhuman elements of the envi-ronment. As Griffin-Pierce (1992) discusses for the Navajo: "Inherent in this use of kin terminology is a recognition of mutual responsibility: nature will take care of humankind if humankind fulfills its kinship responsibilities by taking care of and behaving responsibly towards nature" (27). Looked at in this way, the sky can help a people express and develop their essential humanity.

Clearly, the sky is an awesome presence, difficult to define and comprehend.

RAINBOWS

As anyone who has ever seen one can attest, rainbows are a glori-ous display of nature's beauty. That these prismatic arches appearing magically in the sky should have some cosmic significance is easy to accept. Our modern Western definition of these bands of color as light refracted in water vapor—drops of rain or mist—viewed opposite the sun does little to evoke the excitement or wonder experienced at our first vision of a rainbow, and I suspect it is more with awe than with everyday complacency that many peoples experience this phenomenon.

As described in this chapter's opening vignette, the Bororo liken a rainbow to jure, a giant anaconda, for which they have a great deal of respect. A dance with circular, serpentine movements is also called jure, and is significant as the dance being performed at the beginning of an important myth, which is associated with a boy's coming of age, the procuring of ritually significant rattles, and the naming of certain stars and constellations (see Fabian, 1992:chapter 2). Although the full cultural significance of the analogy between anaconda, dance, and rainbow may be unclear, as I suggest in the field sketch at the start of this chapter, a significant correlation exists between perceptions of the anaconda and (particularly) male vigor and maturity. Together, these symbolic elements resonate with Bororo concepts and perceptions of beauty, fecundity, and vitality as expressed both naturally and culturally.

The snake and rainbow connection occurs elsewhere in South America. To the west of the Bororo, runa in the Peruvian Andes consider rainbows to be giant, two-headed serpents, whose arching bodies connect their heads located in two springs. Overall, the associations with water and the rainy season are primal (Urton, 1981:87–88). Among the equatorial Eastern Timbira of Brazil, the rainbow is called "person of the rain," and is perceived to "have its two ends resting in the open mouths of two sucuriju snakes, which themselves yield rain" and may also be an avenue by which snakes ascend to the sky (Nimuendajú, 1946:234). It seems to be viewed by these people as a sign that the rain has ceased.

In North America the snake and rainbow association is not apparent. According to Farrer, the Mescalero Apache of the Southwest say that Rainbow was created on the First Day of creation, along with the other elemental entities of Sun, Mother Earth, Moon, Stars, and Wind by the Eternal Power. In their creation account, the Eternal Power tells Rainbow, "You will remind Man of My beauty" (1991:23–24). Also in the Southwest, a Pima song of the saguaro wine ceremonial, which "heralds the beginning of the new year," includes the line "To the land of rainbows I'm going," interpreted to allude to the land of the dead, a trance state, and the "Rainhouse" at the eastern horizon perceived as "the source of fertility and renewal" (Hoskinson,1992:135–36). Over in the southeast, Cherokee tradition identifies both the rainbow and lightning as the beautiful raiment of Thunder and his two sons the Thunder Boys. Rainbow has by extension a relationship with storms and the thundering voice of large waterfalls, and must be respected such that a breach in the taboo against pointing to one directly will result in a swollen finger joint (Mooney, 1982 [1900]:257). Not much on the rainbow is recorded from Arctic sources, but the Inuit in Igloolik distinguish in terminology a full rainbow with both ends touching the ground or horizon, from a partial one. The full rainbow is likened by name to the "entrance to an igloo," although this association is not clear. Some Inuit peoples apparently used the rainbow as an omen, its height and steepness indicating either good or bad fortune (MacDonald, 1998:159).

SOLAR AND LUNAR HALOES

While the sun and moon are of obvious significance for time reckoning as well as for various other cosmological contexts, various observable atmospheric phenomena directly associated with the sun and moon are also watched with interest by many sky observers. Most frequently such phenomena take the shape of haloes of colored light around either the sun or moon. In Western science these *solar* and *lunar haloes* are considered to be the reflection and refraction of light through or by ice particles in Earth's atmosphere. Limited data on these phenomena exist in the published literature. The *Enciclopédia Bororo I* (Albisetti and Venturelli, 1962), for example, glosses two relevant expressions, *ari ure marido mugudo tui-oku* (moon, circle/wheel around it) and *meri ure marido mugudo tui-oku* (sun, circle/wheel around it) as lunar halo and solar halo, respectively, without additional information.

When other accounts of native peoples mention their attentiveness to such haloes or rings, it is usually in association with weather prediction. Not surprisingly, in the far north where weather can change dramatically and quickly to life-threatening proportions, we find both solar and lunar rings and similar phenomena are noted and used for weather forecasting. Among the Kutchin on and around the Yukon River and the Arctic Circle, for example, a gray ring around the moon (and possibly the sun) in winter foretells snow and warmer temperatures, but a colored ring or "rainbow" around the moon (or possibly the sun) in the same season predicts a sharp, cold wind. A red ring, however, around the sun in summer means rain, while a nondescript "yellow thing" around the moon presages hot weather. A phenomenon described as a "circle and horns" around either the sun or the moon is a dire signal of a very harsh winter with freezing and starvation, a warning to collect as much food and supplies as possible (Osgood, 1936:92, 98). Among the Inuit, solar haloes as well as the related *sun dogs* or *parhelia* (singular, parhelion, from the Greek for "beside the sun"), which are often colorful, bright spots to either side of the sun, are usually said to be harbingers of stormy weather (MacDonald, 1998:158).

To the south, the Plains Crow say that a halo around the sun or moon tells them that cold is coming. Sun dogs are also mentioned by the Crow as a predictor of a change in weather, with heat being predicted if the sun dogs are minor, cold if they are large and broad. Besides the weather, the presence of sun dogs suggests to the Crow a good time to do stealthy acts (such as sneaking up on the enemy), a time of decision making, and an indication of fertility and an easy childbirth for those who are pregnant (McCleary, 1997:105).

In the South American Tropics in the Andes Mountains, the Quechua-speaking runa also observe solar and lunar haloes with interest in weather forecasting, specifically related to rain. As Urton (1981) reports from Misminay, "The prediction of rain by haloes is done by judging the relative size of the halo: small ones precede rain by a number of days, larger ones by only a day or two" (91). Such haloes as seen in the Andes seem to be related conceptually to rainbows and other atmospheric phenomena and may be identified on the basis of color and seasonality, as well as having probable gender differentiation. Of interest here is that at least one Western scientific study has shown that "haloes around the sun or moon are accurate portents of rain at least seven times out of ten" (as reported in Urton, 1981:213:chapter 4, n. 3), substantiating the native observations and interpretations of such phenomena.

OTHER NIGHTTIME CELESTIAL PHENOMENA

In chapter 5, I suggested that the stars represent temporal regularity and continuity in the night sky, in contrast to the relatively irregular and discontinuous movements of planets. A further contrast is evident, however, in the generally erratic appearance of meteors or shooting stars and comets. *Meteors* (shooting stars or falling stars), are bits of interplanetary debris, such as stone or metal ores, in our solar system that ignite from the friction of collision with our atmosphere and appear briefly, if occasionally brilliantly, as a flash of light in the night sky. A *comet* is a much more distant and occasional feature of the night sky, a ball of frozen matter and gas, that becomes visible and displays a characteristic tail as it burns while nearing the sun in its orbit. Besides their technical differentiation, these two celestial phenomena (meteors and comets) also vary dramatically in their frequency of occurrence: meteors can be seen on virtually any clear night but vanish quickly, while comets appear only rarely, but may stay visible for a number of successive nights.

Although prominent meteor showers, such as the Perseids in early August and the Geminids in December, are regular annual features, the potential for seeing a shooting star on virtually any clear night imparts a particularly random quality to these celestial features. This (potentially frequent or heavy) randomness, as punctuations in the otherwise regular line-up of stars, readily lends itself to application in prognostication. For the Bororo, shooting stars are called *aroe kodu* or "flight of the soul," and are considered an ill omen, associated with the theft of someone's soul by a malicious spirit, and requiring a specific type of shaman to interpret and/or intervene. Among runa in the Andes, shooting stars will be observed by a native priest to divine the whereabouts of a lost or stolen article as indicated by the meteor's point of origin and trajectory. Also, some priests are able to divine for such things as death and illness "by interpreting the final burst of light given off by a shooting star" (Urton, 1981:92). In the northern Tropics throughout the Mayan area, "meteors are thought to be evil omens forecasting sickness, war, and death" (B. Tedlock, 1992:181). Further north among the Ojibwa, meteors (and comets) traditionally were regarded as omens serious enough to require interpretation by a specific type of shaman, one with responsibility for celestial time reckoning (Conway, 1992:248).

But not all peoples regard shooting stars with such dismay. The tropical Timbira, for example, interpret a shooting star as a "star running to the other side of the sky to get married," a reflection of their own pattern of **moiety exogamy** (a rule requiring marriage into the half of the village opposite to that into which one is born; Nimuendajú, 1946:233). Comparably, the Crow of the northern Plains interpret an individual shooting star as the movement of a star being "from one place in the sky to another" (McCleary, 1997:97). An entire and particularly dramatic meteor shower observed by the Crow in 1833, however, brought considerable fear and earned that year the name of "The Year The Stars Fell" (97).

Meteors are well known in the Arctic, where some groups distinguish types on the basis of size and brightness, and often conceptualize the dazzling displays as "feces of the stars" (MacDonald, 1998:141–43). Rather than as a tool for prognostication, shooting stars in the Arctic seem more commonly to be perceived as blessings of cosmic power, capable of bestowing "remarkable powers and abilities on the humans with whom they come in contact" (144). Specific shamanistic prowess is believed to derive from such encounters.

Comets appear much less frequently than do meteors and consequently are less likely to be the topic of ethnographic study. Nevertheless, some data exist. The Bororo have a term for comets, (I)Kuieje Ukigareu, "the tailed star," but I have no other information about them. Curt Nimuendajú (1946), however, describes the reaction of great alarm to the 1910 appearance of Halley's comet by the Eastern Timbira: "At that time a precentor [ceremonial leader] . . . revived the song: 'The star is already setting (the Earth) aflame!' [alternatively: 'The star causes a conflagration.']" (190, 233). The song was accompanied by a dance led by men with rattles, all in an apparent effort to forestall the comet's tail setting the world afire.

Concern and fear seem common among native peoples witnessing comets. On the North American Plains the Crow talk of Halley's Comet in 1910, which they called Ihkachíishpishe, "Star with a Tail," saying that "it was dangerous, it could've ended our lives" (McCleary, 1997:95). Due to the threat, the tribal elders stayed awake singing songs while dressed in their best clothes, as "they wanted to be well dressed and with friends singing joyous songs" if the night was their last (96). But by the appearance of another comet (Hyakutake) in 1996, the Crow were no longer afraid, meeting it "with curiosity, wonder, and much discussion" (97). In at least one tribe's lore, that of the Ojibwa, fear of comets is justified by an earlier experience, when a "Long Tailed Heavenly Climbing Star" came down and burnt everything on the ground, literally making the world a different place (Conway, 1992:243–46). An Ojibwa prophecy says that Comet will destroy again.

Different from the other celestial phenomena mentioned above and generally limited to higher latitudes is the **aurora borealis**, literally from Latin "northern dawn," more commonly known as the "northern lights" (also note a corresponding southern phenomenon, **aurora australis**). The occurrence of this dramatic display of colored bands, waves and streamers of light at extreme latitudes indicates a relevance to the magnetic poles, and our Western explanation is of charged particles within the Earth's magnetic field, perhaps interacting with various gases to produce the differently colored lights. Obviously visible to Arctic peoples, the northern lights are characterized consistently there "as spirits of the dead playing a game of football, usually with a walrus skull for a ball" (MacDonald, 1998:149). Inuit report hearing a swishing sound with auroral displays, and often fear the manifestation as potentially harmful to individuals (149). The Crow on the northern Plains, on the other hand, descriptively and appreciatively call the lights *awáxkowaasaashiia*, "lights shining from the sky," and perceive in them colors, shapes (such as tipis) and also sound. For the Crow, their appearance presages cold weather (McCleary, 1997:99).

EXERCISE: OBSERVING OTHER CELESTIAL PHENOMENA

Since observations of the various phenomena discussed above are not easily planned, you will mainly have to trust to luck and good timing to connect. Use your observation notebooks for any sightings, following the standard procedures of complete information for an entry including date, time, direction you face to observe the phenomenon, its location in azimuth and altitude, and the position/place from which you observe it. Draw what you can, and include a descriptive text where relevant. Be careful in observing solar haloes or sun dogs, as direct observation of the sun with the unaided eye can damage your eyesight (normal sunglasses are NOT adequate protection for sun viewing).

For each phenomenon note color(s) and if possible length of duration (time). For a rainbow, can you see a double? If so, how do the two compare? What is its association with rain and the sun? If you see sun dogs or haloes, is there a weather change afterwards, and if so, what kind? For shooting stars, the months of August and December offer very good potential; can you tell an area of the sky that seems to be the center or origin for a meteor shower? If a comet should appear, how long does it remain visible? What are changes in its appearance and position over time? Is it visible in the daytime?

The topics for observation in this chapter will help encourage your attentiveness to the sky at times other than those you may have selected for regular observations. While not the primary targets for astronomical study, such phenomena nevertheless may have significant meaning in a people's belief system, or may simply be viewed with appreciation or awe in a shared human response to natural wonders.

Chapter Seven

Ethnoastronomical Fieldwork

Air pressure in the sultry September afternoon was building toward a thunderstorm, which villagers expected any day. Such is the precursor of the return of the rainy season, and as the dry season wound to its end, so did our field stint.

I sat in the stuffy interior shade of our small palm-covered house, damp with perspiration. My principal informant, an elder of the Paiwoe clan, sat near me ramrod straight and enjoying a hand-wrapped cigarette I had given him. He hawked and spat through his nearly toothless gums into our smoldering fire, a habit with which he frequently punctuated our conversation and the silent pauses in-between. Pen in hand, I was going over notes I had gotten from him in earlier interview sessions, attempting to clarify points and prompting his translation of various passages in Bororo.

Looking at my pile of notebooks and scattered papers, he shook his head disparagingly.

"You don't have enough," he chided in his fluent and colloquial Portuguese.

"What do you mean?" Taken aback, I was jarred by his comment from any semblance of attitude approaching that of an "objective" scientific researcher.

"That other one, he had much more," he said, motioning with his callused hand above our crude table to what would have been a veritable mound of field notes. This was not the first time he had mentioned working previously with an anthropologist.

It seemed to get hotter and thicker in the hut. I had nothing to say. My several variously colored notebooks were all bent and worn, some of them sweat-stained from being carried folded in a trousers' pocket day after day. To me, their painstakingly recorded contents seemed a prodigious effort.

85

I looked at him, and saw for the thousandth time the outline of his dark and weathered features; his black hair cut traditionally over his eyes, then to his ears at the temples, and hanging squarely about his shoulders; and the feathered earrings threaded through his pierced earlobes. He was right, I knew: there was so much more to learn, to understand, even in his mundane aspects of general appearance. My field techniques had been developed with much trial and error and a delicate balance between active participation in daily cultural activities and formal recording of observations and interviews. And then there were the days when my wife and I had idled about in a hot and malnourished stupor.

But he was right, so I nodded.

"Well, so let's do some more . . ."

When conducted properly, **_ethnography_** provides valuable information about societies and cultures and their perspectives on the world. These perspectives and data help all of us understand more of what it means to be human and can help bridge cultural divides. As such, good ethnographic research is of value not only to the fieldworker or academic discipline, but also to those sharing their knowledge, and to the broader body of human society outside the research area. Ethnographic fieldwork occurs in many different contexts. I have worked in a Bororo village in the tropical savanna of Brazil, in a Peruvian town near the city of Cuzco high in the Andes Mountains, in the bustling metropolises of São Paulo, Brazil, and Osaka, Japan, and among rural Cherokee near Tahlequah, Oklahoma. Preparations and materials needed for effective living and field study in these different places can be as varied as are the places and peoples themselves.

WHAT IS NEEDED

All ethnographers need a fairly standard set of equipment for their field research. Such a set should include video and/or photographic equipment (including different lenses, film speeds, and if possible a Polaroid for instant photos, which are great gifts for the people so graciously allowing you to snap their pictures), a lap-top computer or other typing and information-storing device, a portable tape recorder with a good recording feature and numerous cassettes, plenty of notebooks, pocket-size and larger (and perhaps file cards), along with writing implements, and a generous supply of extra film and batteries. Decisions on equipment brought and used will depend on the specific research conditions and circumstances, including permissions and receptivity of your hosts, research budget, available resources, and personal preferences of the researcher.

Of course, in every field context you must have your personal and professional integrity with you at all times, maintaining the highest standard of ethical behavior (for information on ethics in anthropological fieldwork, see the statement of the AAA Code of Ethics [adopted in 1998], obtainable at *www.ameranthassn.org/committees/ethics/ethics.htm*). Being a good human first and an ethnoastronomer or ethnographer second is important: too many native peoples have expressed disturbance at the manner of involvement of anthropologists in their lives. While many anthropologists have provided valuable services for native peoples, the record is mixed; positive examples do not help much when a potential consultant, like a Cherokee man to whom I was introduced, exclaims, "And who did you exploit for your Ph.D.?!?" Only by consistently putting first the people with whom we are working can we overcome such negative stereotyping.

Ethnoastronomers have some specific equipment and resource needs. For starters, no matter how well you think you know the sky and what is in it, you should have along with you a basic guide to celestial phenomena, such as *A Field Guide to the Stars and Planets* (in the Peterson Field Guide Series; Menzel, 1964), as well as an adjustable star chart for the latitude at which you will be working. (The publishers of *Sky and Telescope* stock such adjustable charts, including plastic options that ideally stand up to moisture and other imperfect fieldwork conditions.) For sessions in which actual identification of nighttime celestial phenomena occurs, a high-powered flashlight that sends out a narrow beam is quite effective at "pointing out" specific stars or other bodies, provided this is acceptable to your informants/consultants. In order to make notes or check a star chart, however, you will need a filtered light so that you will not lose your darkness-adapted sight every time you have to record or check data. So either have two flashlights—one that is filtered and one that is bright and ready for pointing at the stars—or a fairly quick and easy way to adapt the single flashlight to note-taking and chart-checking, such as a rubber band with which to affix a piece of red cellophane over it. Do not forget extra batteries. In order to facilitate recording data, you may want to have prepared data-entry sheets that include places for such critical information as date, time, location, informant, and primary celestial identification. For extended sessions of nighttime sky viewing it becomes more comfortable to lie down, and if you do, a mat, blanket, or groundcover is advisable. And it goes without saying to dress for the weather: I have rarely been so cold as I was as an observatory attendant in the open air in upstate New York winters, and good data are hard to get with your extremities numb and your teeth chattering.

THE METHODS OF RESEARCH

Ethnoastronomical field research shares much in common with ethnographic research in general. In order to learn a people's astronomy, a qualitative research strategy is fundamental. The principal qualitative methodological construct to work within is that of participant observation, the very backbone of cultural anthropology. H. Russell Bernard (1994) describes the binary features of this challenging methodology:

> Participant observation involves establishing rapport in a new community; learning to act so that people go about their business as usual when you show up; and removing yourself every day from cultural immersion so you can intellectualize what you have learned, put it into perspective, and write about it convincingly. (137)

Rapport building is critical to successful participant observation, and is a personal process that weds your personality as researcher with the sensibilities and dynamics of the people with whom you are working. Rapport can be facilitated by a helpful introduction from a mutual acquaintance (sometimes a prerequisite for acceptance), but with or without this, the process of being accepted or at least tolerated by a group usually requires a continuing respectful presence among the group. Effort should be made to enter into daily tasks and activities with the group. While you are doing this, you can also perform basic projects such as mapping the area/community and orienting yourself to the local sky. Ethnoastronomical data are generally acquired through conversing with specific informants, and rapport with these informants or consultants is fundamental to productive interactions. Interviewing skills are also important. Interviews range anywhere from the formal, structured, directive interview to the informal, unstructured, and non-directive conversation. The format and style of interviewing informants will necessarily depend upon proclivities of both researcher and informant, as well as other context- and data-sensitive needs, and will almost certainly involve considerable "trial and error" efforts; your interview style is likely to evolve and adapt over time.[1]

Of course, one of the most important aspects to ethnoastronomical fieldwork is the accurate identification of celestial objects as perceived by the people with whom you are working, so honing your own knowledge of the sky prior to arriving in the field is a prerequisite.

RECORDING YOUR DATA

It is paramount to record information obtained in the field as close to the time of getting it as possible. In most cases, distortion and loss of your data is proportional to the time between receiving the data and recording it. You owe it to yourself, your informants/consultants, and your discipline to develop accurate and timely data-recording strategies.

Nighttime sessions involving stellar identifications offer some unique challenges. For one thing, recording data in the dark is always a problem. Providing enough light to see for data-recording purposes can interfere with the night vision so critical to successful stargazing. This is partially resolved by using a filtered flashlight, as suggested previously. However, there can still be problems: you may need to hold the light, write down information, and consult a resource like a sky chart all at the same time. Experience will help you manage these challenges.

Fieldwork conditions, informants, and situations vary, even day-to-day, and you may be getting some of your richest information from someone you have very limited access to while in impromptu circumstances. You may find yourself lacking star charts, flashlight, or observation-recording sheets when you need them. But versatility and adaptability are two of the traits most indispensable in any ethnographic fieldwork! To the extent possible, you always should carry a small pocket notebook and pencil with you while in the field. Of course, there may be times when it is physically impossible to take notes—as when swimming through rivers on fishing jaunts with the Bororo. In the event of such dire but data-filled circumstances, do what you can to grasp as much of it as possible as it is occurring. If you have writing implements, but little time or other unfavorable circumstances, then jot down key words and draw what you can of the pertinent object or phenomenon. If you find yourself utterly unable to record, try to lock the data in your mind with mnemonic schemes of any kind that work for you. Then, as soon as possible following the event, record as much of it as you can. Be sure to mark as questionable whatever is so, either because you did not get it all or because you lost some of it since the telling. Try to corroborate the information and clear up details in later sessions.

Since research of any kind is the search for meaningful patterns, corroboration of data is important. One strategy to enhance the reliability and credibility of your field data is to ask the same questions of different informants on separate occasions, comparing their responses afterward. Sometimes this strategy, though, is impractical in that informants may feel that their responses either are not being taken seriously, or that the information they provide is not considered as valuable as that of another. Another strategy is to ask similar information of the same informant during different sessions. The overall quality of your data and your field experience in general can be enhanced by regular review of your data: study it, critique it, label and organize it, find the holes in it, the inconsistencies and the connections. Probe your work, and take the results back to your informants with new questions for additional productive sky-viewing sessions. As a reminder, context itself is data, so be sure to label your work for details such as time and date, location, and informant(s), and any other pertinent contextual information that can be added. (Since I am focusing on the field research itself, I am not discussing strategies for researching ethnohistoric or other documents, and comparing your data to these other sources of information outside of the field.)

For your sketches of stars and constellations, always include the horizon line for reference (unless you are really working with zenith or near-zenith observations); altitude and azimuth references are a must. Be sure to label your drawings with both the Western and native astronomical identification. You can copy your actual field observations by redrawing them and cleaning up details, but always retain the originals: this is your raw data and may be needed to check against your redrawing for inaccuracies or inconsistencies.

RECEPTIVITY AND CONTROLLING BIAS

Over a century ago, Frank Hamilton Cushing, and later Franz Boas, pioneered a new strategy of ethnographic fieldwork, that in the first quarter of this century was codified by Bronislaw Malinowski (1984 [1922]) into what today we call participant observation. Their model involves long and intensive interaction with the people who were the focus of ethnographic inquiry, including residing among them, actively participating in as well as observing daily activities, and learning to communicate with them in their own language. These strategies were applied so as to achieve what Malinowski calls the "final goal" of the ethnographer: "to grasp the native's point of view, his relation to life, to realise *his* vision of *his* world" (25).

Anthropologists may hotly debate whether this is the ultimate goal of the ethnographer, and if it is, just to what extent any outsider can hope to grasp the native's point of view. After all, how well can any individual realize any other individual's vision of the world? Even so, many anthropologists would agree that an important *goal* of the ethnographer is to *approximate* the native's point of view, to *attempt* to understand and relate his/her vision of the world (native is used here to mean a member of the society in question). These are important ideals to strive for. How can we achieve them?

Since native astronomies are culturally embedded, Malinowski's suggestions on ethnographic field research tactics in general apply to field research in ethnoastronomy. Even to attempt to grasp another people's point of view we must spend quite a bit of intensive time among them, as much as possible eating what they eat, drinking what they drink, doing what they do, speaking their language, and learning to see what they see and how they see it. Critical to success in this endeavor are your attitude and awareness while doing field research.

Our society has enculturated us into seeing the world from a particular perspective. While the perspectives may be different, all societies provide this essential function for their members; it is what helps members survive and interact successfully with each other and with the broader world around them. But to approach the understanding of another people exclusively from our own perspective is ethnocentric, prone to value judgments based on how we have learned to view the world. By definition from an ethnocentric perspective, the different perspectives of others are wrong.

Ethnoastronomers, like all types of ethnographers or field anthropologists, need to control their ethnocentric biases and to approach their work with as open a mind as possible. This means striving for empathetic receptivity and relative objectivity, which is harder than it sounds. The complementary strategy of participant observation is the ideal vehicle by which to achieve both. Immersion or participation is a form of experiential learning by which you improve your sensibilities to the native's perspective. But true ethnographic learning requires a measure of nonjudgmental observation, note-taking, analysis, and cogitation. For example, had I listened with ethnocentric bias to the Bororo who claimed that the moon rises in the west, I would have dismissed the comment as either silly or ignorant. On the other hand, had I simply accepted the statement as unexamined fact, I may have missed the mechanism of apparent lunar motion that informs us of the Bororo view. From either view alone, vital insight would have been lost.

Another way of conceptualizing the complementarity of participant observation, of empathic receptivity, through direct experience and through examining cultural bias, is by invoking the emic and etic perspectives. *Emic* is an actor-oriented or insider's perspective, what Malinowski would call the point of view of the native. From the Bororo emic perspective, for example, "the moon rises in the west." We access this perspective by intensive participation and conversations with our hosts. *Etic* is an observer-oriented or outsider's perspective, from which we try to see and nonjudgmentally understand. For example, I have been taught that the moon revolves around the Earth and that the Earth rotates on its axis, and therefore on any given day or night the moon will appear to rise in the east or at least course in a westerly direction. Taken together, the emic and etic perspectives act like binocular vision to bring depth and dimension to any topic of ethnographic research. I begin to understand that while (etically) the moon on any specific day moves in a westerly direction, (emically) it reappears in the west as a new moon and thereafter waxes and is higher on successive evenings. While technically it helps me to understand the overall celestial movement of the moon, I am also able to grasp a practical sense of the moon's synodical periodicity by emically perceiving the start of a synodical phase by the waxing crescent moon's first appearance low over the western horizon after sunset. Both the emic and the etic perspectives richly contribute to our understanding of the ethnographic present.

A final comment on receptivity. Another facet of receptivity is genuinely wanting to learn (Bernard discusses this as "maintaining naiveté" [1994:149–51]): for example, what or who is the sun for the people with whom you are working? In addition to feeling motivated and enthused, this means taking for granted nothing about what you are learning. Being receptive to other people's knowledge is a challenge that requires effort and experience to refine.

Striving for greater objectivity and receptivity requires you as the researcher to be aware of your state of mind, a veritable Socratic process of enduring value. This takes some conscious management of your thought processes and responses to fieldwork. Frequent critical review of your field notes should help you see where there are gaps or other difficulties with your data and its analysis, with the overall process of living with and learning from your consultants/informants. Examining your work and life in this way should be beneficial beyond fieldwork toward achieving the quality of the examined life.

WHAT IS TABOO

Building rapport is basic to successful fieldwork. Part of establishing good relations with the people with whom you are living and working is gaining their trust. Trust is easier to establish when you do not transgress local taboos. Part of the challenge is learning about taboos before we transgress them. One of the best ways to do this is to observe first and do after. In other words, at least be careful of doing something you have not seen someone else do (and even then, you can unwittingly break a taboo).

Taboos can be almost anything, from avoiding certain kinds of foods or mentioning names of the deceased, to looking someone directly in the eyes when speaking. A particularly difficult taboo for ethnoastronomers is one against pointing directly at something (or someone). Sometimes, as among the Crow Indians, it is taboo to point directly at the stars with a finger. Fortunately for Timothy McCleary (1997) who works among the Crow, this taboo is avoidable by using some other object such as a willow shoot (12).

It should go without saying that sensitivity to cultural taboos is fundamental to successful fieldwork. Creative solutions may help get around them in areas of important information (such as using a pointer rather than a finger in referring to specific stars). But if a transgression occurs, do what can be done to remedy any misunderstandings and go beyond it. This may involve repentance and even restitution. Be ready and able to laugh at yourself; if the transgression was not serious, just going along with how ridiculous or hilarious it was for you to break the taboo may be your best bet of going beyond the infraction.

THE IMPORTANCE OF CONTEXT

Try asking someone in the United States to tell you what they do for Thanksgiving when it is May, or what they do on the Fourth of July in December. Most of us are better prepared and more likely to remember details when the context of what we are talking about is at hand. Is it different anywhere else? While working among the Bororo I was unable to get much information about life cycle celebrations until the celebrations themselves occurred. Then not only was I able to see and participate in much of the activity, but also people were more willing to talk about these activities and more informative when they did talk. People generally relate to things contextually, and field data will be richer when gathered with this in mind.

Context may also intersect with taboo. It may be considered inappropriate or taboo to discuss topics not immediately in context. In *Thunder Rides A Black Horse*, for example, Claire Farrer (1996) reports that among the Mescalero Apache, "One only talks about things in context" (35), referring here specifically to "beginningtime stories" told among the Mescalero only during the four-day puberty ceremonial. She notes after one such story, about Rain and Thunder that was told as a thunderstorm was blowing in, "that Apaches know that calling Rain's ritual name in narrative results in calling the physical presence of rain to oneself" (39, n. 5). An implication here is not only the appropriateness of context to what is being said, but managing the consequences of talking about and potentially calling upon oneself something out of context.

"Context" is really contexts, since categories of contexts may overlap and influence what gets said and done. As cited above, certain stories might be told only at a certain time of year and then only with certain meteorological phenomena occurring at the same time. Perhaps some stories are gender-exclusive or are sensitive to place. Others may be told by some members of a people but not by others or in daytime but not at night. For ethnoastronomers, taking note of astronomical information is important in the day as well as at night, in the rainy as well as the dry season, in winter as well as summer. This is another reason why intensive participant observation is important for fieldwork. Only by directly experiencing a variety of different contexts can the researcher learn more fully what goes on in these contexts and have a sense of what is appropriate to each, thereby interacting with people accordingly. Such deep contextual interaction also strengthens our comprehension of the integrated multidimensionality of native cultural systems.

THE GOOD INFORMANT AND MULTIPLE INFORMANTS

To get good and reliable information on any given topic a researcher needs a good and reliable source of information. Not everyone knows the local bus schedule, the quality of a given make of automobile, the value of a specific antique. Some people are just better informed through circumstance or coincidence or training. To get good astronomical information—that is, not only a large quantity of information, but information that is culturally valid—from a certain people, you need an informant or consultant who is astronomically knowledgeable. Other qualities that make a good informant are good communication skills and a willingness to share with you what s/he knows. Indigenous astronomical knowledge, just like other facets of culture, usually is not evenly distributed among a given group of people, especially in the contemporary era and its acculturating pressures. Some effort needs to be put into identifying and locating the "experts." In tribal societies, these are likely to be cultural elders, leaders of songs and ceremonies, storytellers, and shamans; not infrequently, some of these categories overlap.

Whether there are specialists or experts or not, it is wise to work with a number of different informants or consultants: first, more consultants always increase your chances of working with true experts; second, even though the research strategies described here are essentially qualitative, more informants serve as a larger sample, which can enhance the validity of your data and any generalization you make about it. Consulting a number of different informants is especially important for astronomical research since such information may not be codified to the extent that everyone in a specific culture shares only one set of knowledge. Rather, as seems to be true for the Bororo and other peoples mentioned, especially regarding stars, there may be legitimate coexisting sets of information about astronomical topics including different names for stars or constellations and perhaps individual applications of observations made with calendrical functions.

ETHNOASTRONOMY BEYOND ASTRONOMY: CULTURAL INTEGRATION

One common characteristic of culture is that it is "integrated." That is, there is a tendency for the different aspects of culture "to function as an interrelated whole" (Haviland, 1999:44). This is an important concept to grasp and is particularly relevant in the pursuit of good ethnoastronomy. Astronomy, especially outside of the modern West, is integral to many other facets of culture and needs to be appreciated and acquired in this capacity.

For the Bororo, as has been seen in the preceding chapters, astronomy relates to the calendar and seasonality as well as day and night time-keeping. It also is used to help locate, orient, and organize villages and is fundamental to directionality and cosmology. In its inclusion in folklore it is often instructive with moral lessons or other guidance. Astronomical knowledge has a role in ceremony, contributes to adequate subsistence, and is even integrated into Bororo social organization. McCleary (1997) also found the integratedness of astronomy to be true among the Crow: "It was often confusing to Crow elders how or why stars or other celestial phenomena would be considered apart from their interconnectedness with the rest of the natural and spiritual world. In fact, it eventually became apparent that the two should not nor could not be separated" (8–9). And as Farrer (1996) reports for the Mescalero: "Apachean religious philosophy . . . is based on astute observations of the natural universe and the sky in particular . . . From the observations, both the philosophy (principles and concepts of knowledge) and epistemology (origin of human knowledge) of the people were devised" (70).

As ethnoastronomers working from an anthropological perspective, we must not only be sensitive and receptive to the astronomical knowledge of a people, but understand how this knowledge contributes to and is integrated with other facets of culture.

RESEARCH DESIGN AND SAMPLE QUESTIONS

In order to learn a meaningful set of patterns from those with whom we are working, our research needs to start with a specific plan of action. It is important to plot out what you will do when and with whom, making arrangements accordingly; this allows the most efficient and productive use of your and their time, energy, and resources. Of course, few things in life go as planned, and, especially in the course of ethnographic fieldwork, your plans and activities should be flexible and adaptable to the ongoing and daily circumstances of life. Especially since context is so significant to quality data, you want to be able to take advantage of unusual events or opportunities when they arise, which may result in a last-minute change of plans. It is also advisable to build in a certain amount of flextime into your research agenda, to enhance your ability to go with the flow of "native" life.

Obviously when researching astronomy, long and frequent nocturnal outdoor sessions are a fact of life. Your schedule (including sleep patterns) and preparations (such as the necessary equipment to make night sessions productive) must take this into account. For the most complete ethnoastronomical knowledge, frequent observation sessions should be carried on with good informants, ideally over the course of a year for phenomena with annual cyclicities. Subsequent visits will deepen your rapport and understanding and may help to uncover data on longer-than one-year cycles. Still, an ethnoastronomical project of any length can produce valuable results.

While some night time needs to be set aside for actual stargazing, on other nights or during periods of the night when you are not observing, there may be other important behavior that has astronomical relevance to note and record. On the other hand, diurnal astronomical observations are also important, such as the sun and its course, daytime lunar observations, and atmospheric or other celestial phenomena, while the timing of virtually any activities might have astronomical relevance. Daytime may also be the preferred time for going over your notes and drawing up new topics or issues for future observation or interview sessions, as well as for engaging in appropriate rapport-building and seasonally- or temporally-related behavior and events. These latter activities will enrich your relationships, are critical to any efforts to access the native view of things, and will reassure those among whom you are working of your identity as a "normal" (if still odd) human being.

Asking questions is a basic strategy of gathering data in the field, although this practice may be considered rude in some cultures. If asking questions is a methodological option, still understand that some questions can be more productive than others. Basic terms and concepts need to be acquired for referring to the sky and its varied phenomena, as well as for directionality, temporality/seasonality, and cosmology (including the "big" questions, such as "Why are we here?", as well as positioning where "here" is, terrestrially and cosmically). Basic start-up questions such as "What is that?"(or "What do you call that?"), while pointing (if allowed), can get things going. If asking questions proves to be nonproductive (even in societies where it is not rude, our anthropological tendency to inquire should be tempered short of becoming a nuisance), perhaps simply listening more attentively and receptively will bring results. Overall, you will need to find the style of communication and interaction that works best for you in your research context.

Basically, all ethnoastronomical research must pursue two basic concerns:

1. What is the astronomical system: who observes what, when, where, how, and why (or what is observed when, where, how, why, and by whom)?

2. How/in what ways does what is found in #1 above relate to
    other components of culture?

Keeping these in mind, and to provide some starting point for
your ethnoastronomical research, I make suggestions below on topics
organized similarly to the order of the previous substantive chapters.
These are intended less as a paradigm for research inquiries and more
as simple stimulation for your own research agenda. For all topics, be
as attentive and accurate as possible in recording ***ethnosemantically***
(in the natives' own language, with careful glosses) the pertinent terms
for all astronomical phenomena.

The sun: Of particular note seems to be the transition from day to
night and night to day. Sunset and sunrise and their significance for
local culture should be noted.

- What cultural use is made of such observations?
- Is solar position used to tell time on a daily basis? (If so, note
  method.)
- Is movement of the sun marked for seasonal activities? What
  are the seasons, and what activities are associated with each?
- Do other dates and their activities depend on solar observations?
- Are there day counts or periodicities that rely on solar obser-
  vation?
- Are solstices observed?
- Equinoxes?
- In the Tropics: zenith passages? Is passage through the nadir
  a relevant concept? (You may need to determine the likely
  positions for sunrise and sunset on dates of nadir crossing to
  determine significance.)
- In the Arctic, how are the summer period of light and the win-
  ter's great darkness perceived and understood? How do people
  relate to the circumpolar sun?
- Is a solar eclipse known, and how is it explained?

For all of the above, note how the sun is observed, from where, and
by whom. The use of any devices, such as a gnomon or shadow-casting
device, and long-distance sighting features should be carefully recorded.

You should inquire about who or what the sun is. Record any relevant folklore as well as pertinent social relationships. What is the
native explanation for solar movement? Where is the sun at night, and
how does it get from west back to east?

Directionality is another topic that may be related to solar observation. What are the principal directions, and how are they culturally significant? (For example, are structures associated with or oriented to specific
directions? Colors? Animals? Social groups? Cosmological principles?)

What relevant cultural practices are associated with all/any of the above?

The moon: Universally, the synodical period of the moon, that is its phases, is of interest to humans. But significance of the moon's position and sidereal relationships to stars should also be checked.

- What are the culturally relevant lunar phases?
- What activities coincide with what phases?
- What positions of the moon are noted? Especially regarding the reappearing new moon, is its angle, size, or brightness significant?
- Is there a system of moon-related months? Are these intercalated with the solar or tropical year? What cultural practices are associated with lunar months?
- Are lunar conjunctions with stars/planets noted, and if so, with what significance?
- Is a lunar eclipse known, and if so, how is it explained?

For all of the above, note how they are observed, from where, and by whom. What relevant cultural practices are associated with all/any of the above?

You should inquire about who or what the moon is. Record any relevant folklore as well as pertinent social relationships. What is the native explanation for lunar movement? What is its perceived relationship to the sun? Are there significant gender associations with the moon (or sun or other astronomical phenomena, for that matter)?

The stars: The appearance of the first stars of the evening or of those in the brightening predawn is often important for time reckoning or even gauging seasonality.

- On any given night, what stars/constellations can be named?
- What stars/constellations seem to have the greatest cultural significance?
- Is the celestial pole noted?
- Are heliacal risings and settings important?
- Which stars are used to tell night time?
- What seasonal associations are made with the stars/constellations?
- Is there an ecliptic-like path noted among the stars?
- What is the Milky Way? Are its dark areas observed as "constellations"?

For all of the above, note how they are observed, from where, and by whom. What relevant cultural practices are associated with all/any of the above?

You should inquire about who or what the stars are. Record any relevant folklore as well as pertinent social relationships. What is the native explanation for stellar movement?

The planets: Understanding native concepts relevant to the planets depends to a significant extent on your basic comprehension of planetary identifications, locations, and cycles.

- What planets are observed and why?
- If Venus and/or Mercury are identifiable, are they recognized as the same entity in the evening and in the morning?
- Are the planets as a group distinguished from the stars?
- If there is a "morning star" or "evening star" observation, is it exclusively a planet? Can it be any planet? Any bright star?
- Is there a classification for inner/inferior and outer/superior planets?
- Is there awareness of retrograde motion?

For all of the above, note how they are observed, from where, and by whom. What relevant cultural practices are associated with all/any of the above?

You should inquire about who or what the planets are. Record any relevant folklore as well as pertinent social relationships. What is the native explanation for planetary movement?

Other celestial phenomena: Empathetic receptivity is particularly productive in this broad, general category, since ethnosemantic domains probably exist with corresponding cultural categories not coherent or congruent to domains or categories in our Western system. Here, especially, we need to be open to what the native has to tell us.

- What is the sky? How is movement across it by astronomical objects explained?
- What is a rainbow?
- Are lunar or solar haloes (and/or "sun dogs) observed? What do they mean?
- What is a shooting star/meteor, and what is the reaction to one when directly observed?
- Are comets known? What are they? What do they mean?
- What is the aurora borealis (or australis) and its meaning?

For all of the above, note how they are observed, from where, and by whom. What relevant cultural practices are associated with all/any of the above? Record any relevant folklore as well as pertinent social relationships. You will need to determine the relevance of other celestial happenings, such as meteorological phenomena: clouds, rain, thunder, lightning, etc.

To reiterate, the above list is only intended to be suggestive. In fact, limiting yourself to Western constructs may be counterproductive in a truly native setting. Nevertheless, working with and from the set of astronomical constructs with which you are familiar should make for a fruitful beginning. After that, the more culturally sensitive and contextual your inquiries are, the richer your results will be.

Endnote

[1] A thorough discussion of ethnographic research methods is beyond the scope of this work. Many fine texts on anthropological research methods are available. The earlier cited book by Bernard, *Research Methods in Anthropology*, is comprehensive and written in an accessible tone and style. For shorter or early-level college research methods courses with a hands-on approach, a helpful text is *Field Projects in Anthropology: A Student Handbook, Third Edition*, by Julia Crane and Michael Angrosino.

Chapter Eight

Ethnoastronomy in the Context of Human Life

Finally after the dry season fires and drought, the rains had come again. The dust of path and plaza was settled and dark but not yet muddy, and the tired browns of August were giving way to new October green. We had arrived during the rains, and now an annual cycle later we were preparing to depart during them.

The mission jeep's engine hummed and spluttered as its driver waited patiently for the final farewells. Our few belongings were already stowed: we had left virtually everything but fieldnotes, barest necessities, and the clothes on our backs to various friends and families. A number of villagers were there to see us off; the men were mostly stoically aloof while several older women with whom my wife had developed close ties openly sobbed. As we parted and climbed aboard they began a ritualized and yet sincere keening of goodbye.

With both guilty relief and pangs of regret we drove off. It was just yesterday when I had learned that Akiri-doge, the Bororo word for the Pleiades, not only meant "white down" as I had thought, but also referred to the small white and down-like flowers of the *akiri-i* (Bororo) or *angiko* (Portuguese), a common tropical legume. Now I wondered what possible connection there might be between the observed cycle of the Pleiades and that of this forest plant.

As the jeep's engine revved along on our passage over the sodden trail bearing us farther from our year's home and the neighbors and strangers with whom we had shared life, I mused that though a seasonal cycle was completed, my work and my understanding never would be.

While most readers may never actually carry on ethnoastronomical research, I hope that the effort to learn how it might be done and what can be learned from doing it will help stimulate students' empathetic and creative imaginations of the ethnographic other. It strikes me that in our current context of increasing globalization, such an exercise is timely in raising crosscultural awareness and understanding, as well as perhaps enhancing cultural preservation, significant attributes for the contemporary "world citizen" (for more on the relevance of empathetic imagination and world citizenship in our modern world context, see Nussbaum, 1997).

Given the approach taken, however, is it possible to summarize or generalize ethnoastronomy crossculturally, if only in the Americas? Certainly, strong or definitive generalizations are not supportable by the number or type of crosscultural examples provided. An effective generalization about non-Western astronomy is also hampered by the inconsistency of published reports, wherein merely the lack of data should not be taken automatically to mean a lack of cultural interest in the topic, and by the heavy influence of acculturation in many contemporary non-Western societies. Most of the cultural examples that accompany the preceding chapters are from indigenous peoples today or in the recent past that have had to alter significantly their traditional practices due to pressure and/or desire to adopt modern, typically Western, ways. In this sense, culture as a significant variable in astronomical systems is difficult to generalize today, since besides outright genocide and cultural demise there is a certain homogenizing effect that colonialism and more recent trends in development, modernization, and globalization have had and continue to have on indigenous peoples (see some perspectives on this in Bodley, 1999; Maybury-Lewis, 1997; Perry, 1996). But even given these limitations, the urge remains to make some effort toward pulling together, if even mainly from my impressions in reading abundant source material, some general patterns of native, non-Western astronomies.

Astronomical systems the world over observe the same fundamental phenomena of sun, moon, and stars, but specific cultural and geographic contexts shape how these phenomena are observed and what use is made of the observations. Sun and moon are often conceptualized as blood relatives, for example, and yet are contentious as relatives often can be. The moon's synodical periodicity seems universally observed, helping to establish a rhythm within the seasonal flow of time, while the months are commonly identified with characterizations pertinent to environmental conditions with their implied timely cultural activities. A few main stars and groupings of stars, such as Polaris and the Big Dipper in the north, the Southern Cross and α and β Centauri in the south, the Pleiades and Orion throughout, to name some of the most common, are often closely observed. Night and seasonal time are gauged by such observations, while it is also here that the strongest cultural imprint is made in terms of meaningful patterns in the sky as models, symbols, and lessons. The Milky Way in general also falls in this category, with particular attention given to the dark spots that are so prominent in the southern sky. Interwoven with the relative regularity of sun, stars, and even moon are the irregular events, such as eclipses and the movements and positions of planets and the appearances of meteors and comets. Such irregularities commonly have divinatory import, often of impending misfortune. Other manifestations, such as the angle and size of the new moon, sun dogs, solar and lunar haloes, and rainbows, regularly are interpreted for their meteorological messages and may be used to advise specific actions or behavior.

All peoples who practice farming depend to some degree on astronomical observations in timing their planting/economic cycles. This is true for the Bororo, the Quechua runa of Misminay, the Maya, the Puebloans and Navajo of the U.S. Southwest, and the Pawnee, for example. While nonfarming peoples seem to observe the sky less in order explicitly to time economic pursuits, their observations provide one of several indicators for a variety of cultural activities, including that of food procurement or natural resource utilization. This seems particularly evident in some of the month names collected, such as among the Kutchin where the month most closely corresponding to June is the "month of eggs," August and October refer to caribou activities, and September is the month when "the ducks fly south" (Osgood, 1936:90); and among the Lakota who name a Moon for Making Fat (June) and a Moon of Red/Ripe Cherries (July); (Neihardt, 1979 [1932]). Both farmers and food foragers take information gleaned from astronomical observations as significant for subsistence and other concerns, including weather forecasting, as references to important historical and cosmological information, and as patterns for various types of behavior.

Celestial entities are commonly anthropomorphized and/or zoomorphized, and their significance to humans is couched in dynamic and often metaphoric terms. Relationships between humans and these powerful beings are often perceived of and expressed in the grammar of the local kinship system that acknowledges cause-effect influences and reciprocal responsibilities. These relationships are sometimes mediated by specialists, people who watch more attentively the movements of the celestial denizens. Guidance may be sought from celestial beings in prayer or extrapolated from observed patterns, such as "sunwise" directionality in the Plains, the nature of older–younger brother relations as patterned for the Bororo by Sun and Moon, and the Pleiades as a model for unity among the Pawnee and as the epitomy of (desirable) order and balance among the Navajo. Overall among native peoples there is the interest in synchronizing selves, societies, and activities with cosmic beings and powers and their perceived motions and cycles, of fitting in or harmonizing with these forces.

Meanwhile, culture itself and the astronomical observations made may be heavily influenced by a people's location. Another generalization that can tentatively be put forth is one relevant to the latitude of

the observer, at least as seen in the core swatches of the main geographic zones: the Tropics, the Arctic and the Temperate zones. An earlier effort to generalize the astronomies of tropical dwellers primarily in
the Americas (Aveni and Urton, 1982) was moderately successful (see
Gingerich's [1982] summary in the same volume), although its greater
value may have been in allowing for a productive exchange across disciplines on a variety of topics centered in tropical astronomies. But
given this earlier effort, the reports from other volumes already cited
above, and the specific cultural examples provided here, I shall make
another effort to hypothesize about generalities of observation and cosmic directionality as found in these three main zones of latitude.

Tropical astronomy, especially that closest to the equator, is characterized by nearly vertical risings and settings of regular astronomical
phenomena, solar and lunar zenith passages, and generally a very high
sun and moon, both of which travel north and south of the zenith, but
along a relatively limited extent of the horizon. Coincidentally, at least
south of the equator, there is no distinct pole star marking the main
axial point of celestial rotation, which probably contributes to weaken-
ing the south and north as distinct directional points. Together these
observational/environmental factors seem to be associated with a cultural emphasis on up-down motion and the east and west cardinal
directions, with a de-emphasis or a secondary importance given to north
and south as cardinal points. Among the Bororo, for example, although
their moieties occupy the northern and southern arcs of the village circle, north and south as cardinal points remain relatively undeveloped
directional concepts. In contrast, east as either *meri rutu* ("sunrise") or
figuratively *itubore* (the name of a culture hero and the village of the
dead over which he presides), and west as *meri butu* ("sunset") or *bako-
roro* (another culture hero and village of the dead), are fundamental
concepts, as is the zenith, *baru oia* ("center of the sky"). A similar
emphasis on east, west, up, and down is described for the Maya (B. Tedlock, 1992:173–78), while the Quechua runa of Misminay emphasize
intercardinal directionality and the zenith (Urton, 1981).

In contrast to the Tropics, north Temperate Zone astronomy (I
have too little data from the south temperate regions to generalize
there) is characterized by diagonal paths of regular astronomical phenomena, a fixed pole star in the north, and the sun and moon (when
high) limited to the southern portions of the sky. While these bodies
may be limited to the southern sky, however, they travel considerably
farther distances along the horizon north and south of the east and
west cardinal points than is observed in the Tropics. These observations are coincident with attention to the pole star and its circumpolar
companions in systems that commonly recognize and name four dis-
crete cardinal directions. Although details vary, each direction is often
associated with various symbolic categories including color, animals,

powers, and/or other attributes, as is generally true among the Pueblo peoples (Dozier, 1983 [1970]:203–9), the Navajo (Griffin-Pierce, 1992:90–92), the Lakota (Neihardt, 1979 [1932]:chapter 3), and the Seneca (Zolbrod, 1992:44), and is cosmologically symbolized in the "quartered circle" of the Mescalero Apache (Farrer, 1991). With the sun coursing daily from left to right there is emphasis on "sunwise" directionality, and its exclusive presence (when high) in the southern sky may result in such concepts associated with the north as with the Seneca perspective, "the sun isn't there" (see McElwain, 1992:264).

In the far northern Arctic Zone, celestial motion occurs in complete circles around the sky, including a sun that temporarily does not set around the June solstice or does not rise at the December solstice. Rather than an emphasis on east and west as is common in the Tropics, in the far north the definition of east and west by celestial motion is less obvious and more problematic. As MacDonald (1998) describes it, "In high Arctic latitudes, the sun's rising and setting positions during the course of the year range virtually over the entire compass rose, rendering useless the convention so fondly held in more southerly regions that the 'sun rises east and sets west'" (1998:164). The Central Eskimo, for example, discretely name only south "while the other points are called according to the weather prevailing while the wind blows from the different quarters" (Boas, 1888:643). Among the Kutchin, although some terms exist that can be used for the four cardinal directions, when analyzed by Osgood (1936) throughout the Kutchin area they seem to be more specific to local topography, specifically river-related directionality (102), rather than cosmic directionality. Systems of directionality and navigation among the Arctic Inuit, while making some use of solar, lunar, and stellar observations, depend less on cosmic and cardinal directions and more on landmarks and topographic features, wind directions and resulting snowdrifts, and even animal behavior and dream messages (MacDonald, 1998:160–87).

Given the limits of data, I do not wish to overstate my generalizations. After all, among temperate peoples, such as in many (if not all) Pueblo groups, not only four cardinal directions are recognized, but often six (including up and down or zenith and nadir, which resembles the tropical pattern) or even seven directions (including the center). But it seems reasonable that various elements of directionality and cosmology as reckoned by peoples in the main contrasting geographic zones result fundamentally from the application of their astronomical observations. Together, these are integrated into cultural definition and meaning. As Trudy Griffin-Pierce (1992) expresses this for the Navajo, "cosmological order—that is, Navajo conceptions of time and space, as well as perceptions of solar, lunar, and stellar motions—serves as a model for Navajo philosophy" (64). From a case study of the Bororo, whose village shape and orientation, as well as social position-

ing and movement, all bespeak cosmological principles influenced by
basic astronomical observations of especially the sun, I have argued:

> Cosmology is at least in part an understanding of and explanation
> for socioculturally significant perceptions of the environment. Na-
> tives who make use of cosmological considerations in the location,
> orientation, and patterning of their communities are interacting
> with their environments in ways that have gone beyond basic ma-
> terial subsistence and survival. The process of applying cosmologi-
> cal principles in the design and function of living space deeply
> integrates a people in their environment . . . It is at the very least
> a dialectical process of making observations, interpreting perceived
> phenomena, and the reapplication of these interpretations in the
> process of perception and understanding of the environment. Such
> processes socialize a people's environment, as well as functionally
> adapting and integrating a people in it. (Fabian, 1994 [1995]:76)

As attested to in the preceding chapters, native, non-Western peoples commonly take a serious interest in astronomical phenomena as
parts of a dynamically alive and interactive cosmos, a natural world in
which the peoples may see themselves as but a small, interrelated part.
For such peoples, astronomy is generally not an abstract intellectual
pursuit. Rather, "astronomical objects" are more likely perceived as
celestial beings. As with other parts of nature, these beings often are
considered to share bonds of kinship, and their attendant reciprocal
responsibilities and observances, with humans. Small-scale and native
societies tend to look to the celestial entities for guidance and help, to
see in them patterns for behavior, and perhaps to attempt to access
their sacred celestial power for human use.

Not all peoples, of course, observe astronomical phenomena with
the same interest or intensity, nor is knowledge of such phenomena
likely to be shared equally among all members of any given society.
Nevertheless, it seems apparent that knowledge of and familiarity with
locally perceived celestial events can be a significant component in survival and quality of life, especially for small-scale, nonindustrial peoples more fully immersed in nature than is characteristic of the modern
West. For such peoples, awareness of astronomical patterns and cycles
is likely to be part of their detailed knowledge of the environment in
general, including other human groups nearby, the plants and animals
available to them (wild and domestic), water sources and flow, geo-
graphical features, and the main local weather patterns and seasonality. Together, these terrestrial and celestial features form a whole, an
entire cosmos, the very context of human life.

While still too few cultural studies explore deeply the details and
dimensions of indigenous astronomy, happily there is a growing number
of fieldworkers and researchers increasingly knowledgeable about and
sensitive to this major topic. We shall learn best as ethnoastronomers

when we receptively seek to learn what other peoples have to tell us of their systems. Since in intact cultures astronomical knowledge generally becomes integrated with other components into a complex, synergistic whole, to understand and appreciate most fully these systems it is best to approach them holistically. By combining proper astronomical and anthropological preparation, fuller understanding and true appreciation of non-Western astronomy and its contributions to cultural identity, development, adaptation, and survival will be possible.

Glossary

Altitude. In a horizon-based measurement system, the angular distance of an object as measured vertically up from an ideal or flat horizon (0°) to the maximum 90° at the zenith.

Antarctic Circle. The line of latitude (66.5° south latitude) beyond which the sun will not be seen when it reaches its farthest northern limit (on the June solstice).

Anti-Zenith. The point on the celestial sphere beneath an observer and diametrically opposite the zenith (see also *Nadir*).

Archaeoastronomy. The archaeological and historical study of a people's past astronomical knowledge and related practices.

Arctic. The Frigid Zone north of the Arctic Circle.

Arctic Circle. The line of latitude (66.5° north latitude) beyond which the sun will not be visible when it reaches its farthest southern limit (on the December solstice).

Asterism. A grouping of stars not formally recognized in the contemporary Western astronomical taxonomy of constellations (e.g., the Big Dipper, the Pleiades).

Aurora Australis. The "southern lights" (Latin, "southern dawn") of the southern hemisphere, corresponding to the aurora borealis of the north.

Aurora Borealis. Commonly known as the "northern lights" (Latin, "northern dawn"), this phenomenon is a colorful display of bands, waves, and streamers of light especially prominent over and near the north magnetic pole, caused by electrically charged particles (due to solar activity) in the earth's magnetic field, possibly igniting atmospheric gases.

Azimuth. In a horizon-based measurement system, the angular distance of an object as measured from true north (0° [and 360°]) to the right (eastward or clockwise), with east as 90°, south as 180°, and west as 270°.

Celestial Equator. The extension of the earth's equator onto the celestial sphere which marks the earth's plane of rotation on its axis. The celestial equator is at all points 90° from the north and south celestial poles.

Celestial Sphere. An imaginary sphere encompassing all of outer space and centered on an Earth-based observer.

Circadian Rhythms. Biological rhythms exhibiting 24-hour periodicity.

Circumpolar Stars. Stars that, from an observer's latitude, are never seen to set.

Comet. An orbiting celestial body with a solid nucleus and, when close enough to the sun, a vaporous tail, that may be visible for weeks.

Conjunction. The condition when (especially prominent) celestial bodies come into proximity with each other.

Constellation. Formal grouping of stars thought to resemble some culturally-relevant object or entity; in modern Western astronomy, one of 88 such groups into which all visible stars are categorized.

Eclipse. From an observer's perspective, the partial or total obscuring of one astronomical body by another (see also *Lunar Eclipse, Solar Eclipse*).

Ecliptic. The earth's plane of revolution around the sun, perceived on the celestial sphere by Earth-based observers as the apparent path of the sun against the background of stars.

Emic. In anthropology, a culturally-relevant perspective or category derived from an informant, or cultural "insider."

Equator. The imaginary line or great circle on the earth's surface which separates the northern and southern hemispheres and from which degrees of latitude are reckoned.

Equinox. Either of two points on the celestial sphere where the ecliptic intersects the celestial equator, and one of the two times a year (coinciding with this intersection) when the sun, on an ideal horizon, can be observed to rise due east and set due west, with day and night time of roughly equal duration (from the Latin for "equal night"). The *vernal equinox* is the point and time in which the sun, on the ecliptic, intersects the celestial equator moving from south to north, and considered to be the origin point of the ecliptic; the corresponding date around March 22. The *autumnal equinox* is the point and time in which the sun, on the ecliptic, intersects the celestial equator, moving from north to south; the corresponding date around September 22.

Ethnoastronomy. The study of how people who do not ascribe to modern Western astronomical paradigms perceive, understand, and make use of their knowledge of the sky and its phenomena.

Ethnography. As field research, the gathering of data used to produce the systematic description of a culture based on firsthand experience and observation; the work written from this process.

Ethnosemantically. The method of referring to a linguistic, classificatory term or concept of a particular people and culture.

Etic. In anthropology, a perspective or category, usually associated with a theoretical point of view, developed and applied by the researcher as a cultural "outsider."

Frigid Zone. On the Earth, either of the geographic zones which cap the globe, encompassing the area beyond the Arctic Circle in the north and the Antarctic Circle in the south.

Galaxy. A cluster or aggregate of stars, gas, and dust.

Gnomon. A shadow-casting object used to indicate or reckon the passage of time.

Gregorian Calendar. The current Western calendar, increasingly used throughout the world, and dating back to 1582 when its development was sponsored by Pope Gregory XIII.

Heliacal Rise. First rise of a star after its disappearance due to conjunction with the sun.

Heliacal Set. Last set of a star prior to its disappearance due to conjunction with the sun.

Horizon-Based Measurements. System of locating celestial objects in a localized context, using the object's Altitude and Azimuth.

Inferior/Inner Planets. Planets whose orbits lie between Earth and the sun; Mercury and Venus.

Informant. A person with whom an ethnographer interacts and from whom information is acquired while conducting fieldwork.

Intercalary Month. A month (usually based on the synodical lunar period) added to a regular (usually lunar) calendar to synchronize that calendar year with the seasons or solar year.

Intercalation. The insertion of an extra time period into a calendar (see also *Intercalary Month*).

Latitude. Angular distance on the earth's surface north and south of the equator, from 0° at the equator, to 90° at either pole.

Longitude. Angular distance on the earth's surface east and west from the prime meridian at Greenwich, England (0°), up to 180° in either direction.

Lunar Eclipse. The partial or total obscuring of the full moon as it passes through the earth's shadow.

Lunar Halo. Reflection and refraction of moonlight through or by ice crystals in the earth's atmosphere, causing a ring of light to appear encircling the moon.

Meridian. For any Earth-based observer, the imaginary line on the celestial sphere connecting the north point on the horizon with the south, and passing through the zenith. Any astronomical body observed in its regular motion from rise to set will achieve its greatest altitude when on the Meridian; the sun at the meridian defines noon or midday.

Meteor. An astronomical object that is burning from friction as it enters the earth's atmosphere, usually visible as a trail or streak of light in the night sky; also known as a shooting star.

Milky Way. The galaxy in which our solar system is located, and visible at night from Earth as a luminous (or "milky") band.

Moiety Exogamy. A rule requiring marriage into half of the village opposite to that into which one is born; *moiety*: in social systems, one of two halves dividing the society, usually on the basis of rules of descent; *exogamy*: a rule requiring marriage outside of one's specifically defined social group.

Nadir. The point on the celestial sphere directly beneath an observer and diametrically opposite the zenith (see also *Anti-Zenith*).

Nebula. Interstellar dust and/or gas visible as either a luminous or dark patch.

North Celestial Pole. The point on the celestial sphere that is an extension, through the north pole, of the earth's axis of rotation.

Opposition. The point in a superior planet's orbit when it is furthest from conjunction with the sun.

Parhelia. See *Sun Dogs*.

Participant Observation. Ethnographic field research methodology central to cultural anthropology in which the fieldworker actively engages a community through the combination of participatory experience and observation.

Precession. The shift or wobble of the Earth's axis of rotation, causing the nearly 26,000-year cycle of change of position of the celestial poles, as well as the movement westward along the ecliptic and zodiac of the vernal equinox.

Refraction. In astronomy, the apparent elevation in position of an astronomical object seen close to the horizon, as its light is deflected or bent by the earth's atmosphere.

Retrograde Motion. Apparent backward or reversed movement of a superior planet occurring as we on Earth draw nearer and then pass by the planet in our respective orbits.

Revolution. The circling of one astronomical body around another.

Rotation. The spinning of an astronomical object on its axis.

Shooting Star. See *Meteor*.

Sidereal Period. A lunar period or "month" of 27 and 1/3 days based on the moon's observed position with respect to the stars.

Solar Eclipse. The partial or total obscuring of the sun by the moon as it passes between the earth and sun, possible every synodical month at conjunction, or astronomical new moon.

Solar Halo. Reflection and refraction of sunlight through or by ice crystals in the Earth's atmosphere, causing a ring of light to appear encircling the sun.

Solstice. Either of two times a year when the sun arrives at its northern and southern extremes on the ecliptic, resulting in its "standstill" (solstice derives from the Latin for "sun stand"), or no apparent northward or southward movement for several days. The *June solstice* is the sun's northernmost position on the ecliptic, occurring on/around June 21, and known as the "summer solstice" in the northern hemisphere. The *December solstice* is the sun's southernmost position on the ecliptic, occurring on/around December 21, and known as the "winter solstice" in the northern hemisphere.

South Celestial Pole. The point on the celestial sphere that is an extension, through the south pole, of the earth's axis of rotation.

Sun Dogs. Bright spots, usually in a pair on either side of the sun, and often on a solar halo; formally known as "*Parhelia*" (singular, Parhelion).

Superior/Outer Planets. Planets whose orbits lie beyond that of Earth; Mars, Jupiter, and Saturn (for naked eye observers on Earth).

Synodical Period. The month of 29½ days of lunar phases (i.e., from new moon to new moon), based on the moon's position relative to the sun.

Temperate Zone. On the Earth, either of the geographic zones which extend between the Tropic of Cancer and the Arctic Circle in the northern hemisphere, or between the Tropic of Capricorn and the Antarctic Circle in the southern hemisphere.

Torrid Zone (or Tropical Zone or Tropics). On the earth, the geographic zone entering on the equator and stretching between the Tropics of Cancer and Capricorn.

Tropic of Cancer. The line of latitude (23.5° north latitude) that marks the farthest northern limit from which the sun can be seen in the zenith (on the June solstice).

Tropic of Capricorn. The line of latitude (23.5° south latitude) that marks the farthest southern limit from which the sun can be seen in the zenith (on the December solstice).

Zenith. The point on the celestial sphere directly overhead of an observer.

Zodiac. The band on the celestial sphere about 8° to either side of the ecliptic, and the twelve constellations that demarcate it, through which course the sun, moon, and planets.

Bibliography

Albisetti, César, and Angelo Venturelli. 1962. *Enciclopédia Bororo*. Volume I. Museu Regional Dom Bosco, Campo Grande, Mato Grosso do Sul, Brazil.
_____. 1964. *Enciclopédia Bororo*. Volume II. Museu Regional Dom Bosco, Campo Grande, Mato Grosso do Sul, Brazil.
Arias de Greiff, Jorge, and Elizabeth Reichel de Von Hildebrand, eds. 1987. *Etnoastronomías Americanas*. Bogotá: 45th Congress of Americanists, Universidad de los Andes, Centro Editorial, Universidad Nacional de Colombia.
Aveni, Anthony F., ed. 1975. *Archaeoastronomy in Pre-Columbian America*. Austin: University of Texas Press.
_____. ed. 1977. *Native American Astronomy*. Austin: University of Texas Press.
_____. 1980. *Skywatchers of Ancient Mexico*. Austin: University of Texas Press.
_____. ed. 1982. *Archaeoastronomy in the New World*. Cambridge, U.K.: Cambridge University Press.
_____. 1989a. *Empires of Time: Calendars, Clocks and Cultures*. New York: Basic Books.
_____. ed. 1989b. *World Archaeoastronomy*. Cambridge, U.K.: Cambridge University Press.
_____. 1993. *Ancient Astronomies*. Montreal: St. Remy Press and the Smithsonian Institution.
_____. 1997. *Stairways to the Stars: Skywatching in Three Great Ancient Cultures*. New York: John Wiley and Sons.
Aveni, Anthony F., and Gary Urton, eds. 1982. *Ethnoastronomy and Archaeoastronomy in the American Tropics*. New York: Annals of the New York Academy of Sciences, 385.
Bateson, Gregory. 1979. *Mind and Nature: A Necessary Unity*. New York: Bantam Books.
Baity, Elizabeth Chesley. 1973. "Archaeoastronomy and Ethnoastronomy So Far." *Current Anthropology* 14:389–449.
Bean, Lowell. 1992. "Menil (Moon): Symbolic Representation of Cahuilla Woman." In *Earth and Sky: Visions of the Cosmos in Native America Folklore*, Ray A. Williamson and Claire R. Farrer, eds. Pp. 162–83. Albuquerque: University of New Mexico Press.

Benson, Arlene, and Tom Hoskinson, eds. 1985. *Earth and Sky: Papers from the Northridge Conference on Archaeoastronomy*. Thousand Oaks, CA: Slo'w Press.

Berman, Bob. 1995. *Secrets of the Night Sky*. New York: HarperCollins.

Bernard, H. Russell. 1994. *Research Methods in Anthropology: Qualitative and Quantitative Approaches*. Second Edition. Thousand Oaks, CA: Sage Publications.

Blatt-Fabian, Surabela. 1985. Basketry Knowledge and Weaving among Women of the Eastern Bororo of Mato Grosso, Brazil. Unpublished Master's Degree thesis, Department of Anthropology, University of Illinois.

Boas, Franz. 1888. "The Central Eskimo." In *The Sixth Annual Report of the Smithsonian Institution's Bureau of Ethnology*, pp. 399–669, 1884–85, Washington, D.C.: Smithsonian Institution.

Bodley, John H. 1999. *Victims of Progress*. Fourth Edition. Mountain View, CA: Mayfield Publishing Company.

Chamberlain, Von Del. 1982. *When Stars Came Down to Earth: Cosmology of the Skidi Pawnee Indians of North America*. Los Altos: Ballena Press.

_____. 1992. "The Chief and His Council: Unity and Authority from the Stars." In *Earth and Sky: Visions of the Cosmos in Native America Folklore*, Ray A. Williamson and Claire R. Farrer, eds. Pp. 221–35. Albuquerque: University of New Mexico Press.

Colbacchini, Antonio, and César Albisetti. 1942. *Os Bororos Orientais*. São Paulo: Companhia Editora Nacional.

Conway, Thor. 1992. "The Conjuror's Lodge: Celestial Narratives from Algonkian Shamans." In *Earth and Sky: Visions of the Cosmos in Native America Folklore*, Ray A. Williamson and Claire R. Farrer, eds. Pp. 236–59. Albuquerque: University of New Mexico Press.

Cooper, John M. 1917. *Analytical and Critical Bibliography of the Tribes of Tierra del Fuego and Adjacent Territory*. Washington, DC: Smithsonian Institution, Bureau of American Ethnology, Bulletin 63.

_____. 1946. "The Ona." In *Handbook of South American Indians*, Vol. 1, *The Marginal Tribes*. Pp. 107–25. Washington, D.C.: Smithsonian Institution, Bureau of American Ethnology, Bulletin 143.

Crane, Julia G., and Michael V. Angrosino. 1992. *Field Projects in Anthropology: A Student Handbook*. Third Edition. Prospect Heights, IL: Waveland Press.

d'Abbeville, Claude. 1963 (1614). *Histoire de la Mission des Pères Capucins en l'Isle de Maragnan et terres circonvoisins*. Graz, Austria: Akademische Druck-u.

D'Anglure, Bernard Saladin. 1984. "Inuit of Quebec." In *Handbook of North American Indians*, Vol. 5. Pp. 476–507. Washington, D.C.: Smithsonian Institution.

Dozier, Edward P. 1983 (1970). *The Pueblo Indians of North America*. Prospect Heights, IL: Waveland Press.

Fabian, Stephen M. 1982. "Ethnoastronomy of the Eastern Bororo Indians of Mato Grosso, Brazil." In *Ethnoastronomy and Archaeoastronomy in the American Tropics*. Anthony F. Aveni and Gary Urton, eds. Pp. 283–301. New York: Annals of the New York Academy of Sciences, 385.

_____. 1992. *Space-Time of the Bororo of Brazil*. Gainesville: University Presses of Florida.

_____. 1994 (1995). "The Environment as Paradigm for and Reflection of Indigenous Constructs: The Bororo of Mato Grosso, Brazil," *Proceedings of the Indiana Academy of Social Sciences*: 3rd Ser. 29:70–77.

Farrer, Claire R. 1991. *Living Life's Circle: Mescalero Apache Cosmovision.* Albuquerque: University of New Mexico Press.

_____. 1996. *Thunder Rides a Black Horse: Mescalero Apaches and the Mythic Present,* Second Edition. Prospect Heights, IL: Waveland Press.

Farrer, Claire R., and Ray A. Williamson. 1992. "Epilogue: Blue Archaeoastronomy." In *Earth and Sky: Visions of the Cosmos in Native America Folklore*, Ray A. Williamson and Claire R. Farrer, eds. Pp. 278–89. Albuquerque: University of New Mexico Press.

Gingerich, Owen. 1982. "Summary: Archaeoastronomy in the Tropics." In *Ethnoastronomy and Archaeoastronomy in the American Tropics.* Anthony F. Aveni and Gary Urton, eds. Pp. 333–36. New York: Annals of the New York Academy of Sciences, 385.

Griffin-Pierce, Trudy. 1992. *Earth Is My Mother, Sky Is My Father: Space, Time, and Astronomy in Navajo Sandpainting.* Albuquerque: University of New Mexico Press.

Haviland, William A. 1999. *Cultural Anthropology,* Ninth Edition. Orlando, FL: Harcourt Brace and Company.

Hoskinson, Tom. 1992. "Saguaro Wine, Ground Figures, and Power Mountains: Investigations at Sears Point, Arizona. In *Earth and Sky: Visions of the Cosmos in Native America Folklore*, Ray A. Williamson and Claire R. Farrer, eds. Pp. 131–61. Albuquerque: University of New Mexico Press.

Hugh-Jones, Stephen. 1979. *The Palm and the Pleiades: Initiation and Cosmology in Northwest Amazonia.* Cambridge, UK: Cambridge University Press.

Hultkrantz, Åke. 1998 (1987). *Native Religions of North America: The Power of Visions and Fertility.* Prospect Heights, IL: Waveland Press.

Krupp, E. C., ed. 1978. *In Search of Ancient Astronomies.* New York: Doubleday and Company.

Lantis, Margaret. 1984. "Nunivak Eskimo." In *Handbook of North American Indians,* Vol. 5, pp. 209–23. Washington, DC: Smithsonian Institution.

MacDonald, John. 1998. *The Arctic Sky: Inuit Astronomy, Star Lore, and Legend.* Toronto: Royal Ontario Museum, Nunavut Research Insitute.

Malinowski, Bronislaw. 1984 (1922). *Argonauts of the Western Pacific.* Prospect Heights, IL: Waveland Press.

Mary-Rousselière, Guy. 1984. "Iglulik." In *Handbook of North American Indians,* Vol. 5, pp. 431–46. Washington, DC: Smithsonian Institution.

Maybury-Lewis, David. 1997. *Indigenous Peoples, Ethnic Groups, and the State.* Boston: Allyn and Bacon.

McCaskill, Don, ed. 1987 (1989). *Amerindian Cosmology. The Canadian Journal of Native Studies,* Special Issue, 7(2).

McCleary, Timothy P. 1997. *The Stars We Know: Crow Indian Astronomy and Lifeways.* Prospect Heights, IL: Waveland Press.

McElwain, Thomas. 1992. "Asking the Stars: Narrative Indicators of Seneca Hunting Ceremonial." In *Earth and Sky: Visions of the Cosmos in Native America Folklore*, Ray A. Williamson and Claire R. Farrer, eds. Pp. 260–77. Albuquerque: University of New Mexico Press.

Menzel, Donald H. 1964. *A Field Guide to the Stars and Planets.* Peterson Field Guide Series. Boston: Houghton Mifflin Co.

Métraux, Alfred. 1946. "Ethnography of the Chaco." In vol. 1, *The Marginal Tribes,* of *Handbook of South American Indians,* pp. 197–370. Washington, DC: Smithsonian Institution, Bureau of American Ethnology, Bulletin 143.

Miller, Dorcas S. 1997. *Stars of the First People: Native American Star Myths and Constellations.* Boulder: Pruett Publishing.

Miller, Jay. "North Pacific Ethnoastronomy: Tsimshian and Others." In *Earth and Sky: Visions of the Cosmos in Native American Folklore,* Ray A. Williamson and Claire R. Farrer, eds. Pp. 193–206. Albuquerque: University of New Mexico Press.

Montenbruck, O., and T. Pfleger. 1991. *Astronomy on the Personal Computer.* New York: Springer-Verlag.

Mooney, James. 1982 (1900). *Myths of the Cherokee.* Nashville: Charles and Randy Elder—Booksellers, (originally Washington, DC: Bureau of American Ethnology, 1900).

Moore, Patrick. 1980. *The Pocket Guide to Astronomy.* New York: Simon and Schuster.

Neihardt, John G. 1979 (1932). *Black Elk Speaks: Being the Life Story of a Holy Man of the Oglala Sioux.* Lincoln: University of Nebraska Press.

Nimuendajú, Curt. 1946. "The Eastern Timbira." University of California Publications in *American Archaeology and Ethnology,* Vol. 41. Berkeley: University of California Press.

Nussbaum, Martha C. 1997. *Cultivating Humanity: A Classical Defense of Reform in Liberal Education.* Cambridge: Harvard University Press.

Ortiz, Alfonso. 1969. *The Tewa World: Space, Time, Being and Becoming in a Pueblo Society.* Chicago: The University of Chicago Press.

Osgood, Cornelius. 1936. *Contributions to the Ethnography of the Kutchin.* New Haven: Yale University Publications in Anthropology, Number 14. Reprint, New Haven: Human Relations Area Files Press, 1970.

Oswalt, Wendell H. and Sharlotte Neely. 1999. *This Land Was Theirs: A Study of Native Americans.* Sixth Edition. Mountain View, CA: Mayfield Publishing.

Perry, Richard J. 1996. *From Time Immemorial: Indigenous Peoples and State Systems.* Austin: University of Texas Press.

Pinxten, Rik, and Ingrid Van Dooren. 1992. "Navajo Earth and Sky and the Celestial Life Force." In *Earth and Sky: Visions of the Cosmos in Native America Folklore,* Ray A. Williamson and Claire R. Farrer, eds. Pp. 101–30. Albuquerque: University of New Mexico Press.

Ruggles, Clive N., and Nicholas J. Saunders, eds. 1993. *Astronomies and Cultures: Papers Derived from the Third "Oxford" International Symposium on Archaeoastronomy,* St. Andrews, UK, September 1990. Boulder: University of Colorado Press.

"Sky Astronomy Software for Windows," Version 2.0. Astronomical Society of the Pacific (390 Ashton Ave., San Francisco, CA 94112).

Tedlock, Barbara. 1992. *Time and the Highland Maya,* revised ed. Albuquerque: University of New Mexico Press.

_____. 1999. "Maya Astronomy: What We Know and How We Know It." *Archaeoastronomy* 14(1): 39–58.

Tedlock, Dennis. 1996. *Popol Vuh,* revised ed. New York: Simon and Schuster.

Urton, Gary. 1981. *At the Crossroads of Earth and Sky: An Andean Cosmology.* Austin: University of Texas Press.

Wagley, Charles. 1983 (1977). *Welcome of Tears: The Tapirapé Indians of Central Brazil.* Prospect Heights, IL: Waveland Press.

Westrheim, Margo. 1993. *Calendars of the World: A Look at Calendars & the Ways We Celebrate.* Oxford: Oneworld Publications.

Wilbert, Johannes, and Karin Simoneau, eds. 1983. *Folk Literature of the Bororo Indians.* UCLA Latin American Center Publications.

Williamson, Ray A., ed. 1981. *Archaeoastronomy in the Americas.* College Park, MD: Ballena Press/Center for Archaeoastronomy.

_____. 1984. *Living the Sky: The Cosmos of the American Indian.* Boston: Houghton Mifflin.

Williamson, Ray A., and Claire R. Farrer, eds. 1992. *Earth and Sky: Visions of the Cosmos in Native American Folklore.* Albuquerque: University of New Mexico Press.

Zolbrod, Paul. 1992. "Cosmos and Poesis in the Seneca Thank-You Prayer." In *Earth and Sky: Visions of the Cosmos in Native America Folklore,* Ray A. Williamson and Claire R. Farrer, eds. Pp. 25–51. Albuquerque: University of New Mexico Press.

Zuidema, R. Tom. 1981a. "Anthropology and Archaeoastronomy." In *Archaeoastronomy in the Americas,* Ray A. Williamson, ed. Pp. 29–31. College Park, MD: Ballena Press/Center for Archaeoastronomy.

_____. 1981b. "Inca Observations of the Solar and Lunar Passages Through Zenith and Anti-Zenith at Cuzco." In *Archaeoastronomy in the Americas,* Ray A. Williamson, ed. Pp. 319–42. College Park, MD: Ballena Press/Center for Archaeoastronomy.

_____. 1982. "The Sidereal Lunar Calendar of the Incas." In *Archaeoastronomy in the New World,* Anthony F. Aveni, ed. Pp. 59–107. Cambridge, U.K.: Cambridge University Press.

Index